USGBC LEED AP Building Design + Construction Study Guide

Copyright

Disclaimer

U.S. Green Building Council

2101 L Street, NW
Suite 500
Washington, DC 20037

Trademark

ISBN: 978-1-932444-26-1

USGBC LEED AP Building Design + Construction Study Guide Acknowledgments:
The USGBC LEED AP Building Design + Construction Study Guide is a valuable tool for exam candidates planning to attain the BD+C Specialty. We would like to extend our deepest gratitude to those involved in the production of this resource.

PROJECT TEAM

Green Building Services, Inc. (GBS)
Beth Shuck, *Content Developer*
Caitlin Francis, *Project Manager and Content Developer*
Glen Phillips, *Technical Specialist and Content Developer*
Katrina Shum Miller, *Principal in Charge*
Nina Tallering, *Content Developer*

Institute for the Built Environment (IBE)
Brian Dunbar, *Educational Consultant*
Josie Plaut, *Educational Consultant*

NonObvious Solutions
Elizabeth Gast, *Technical Illustrator and Graphic Designer*
Eric von Schrader, *Instructional Designer*

Prometric
Examination Question Writing Training

LEED Curriculum Committee Members
Draft reviews

USGBC Staff
Karol Kaiser, *Director of Education Development*
Jacob Robinson, *Project Manager*

MATERIALS AND RESOURCES

INDOOR ENVIRONMENTAL QUALITY

INNOVATION IN DESIGN & REGIONAL PRIORITY

APPENDIX

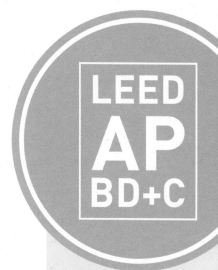

CREDENTIAL OVERVIEW

Congratulations on your decision to pursue the LEED Accredited Professional (AP) Building Design + Construction credential. You are positioning yourself within the marketplace as a professional who is committed to keeping up with current trends and best practices.

As you prepare for the exam, you will be taking what you already know about LEED and green building and developing greater proficiency in an area that is specific and relevant to your line of work.

Accreditation will certify that you have the knowledge and skills necessary to participate in the LEED application and certification process, hold a firm understanding of green building practices and principles, and are familiar with LEED requirements, resources, and processes.

Best of luck on the exam!

GETTING STARTED ON YOUR LEED AP BC+C CREDENTIAL

Earning the LEED AP BD+C credential requires passing a two-part exam:

PART 1: (Also see the Green Associate credential.) A two-hour exam. Passing Part 1 attests to the candidate's general knowledge of green building practices for both commercial and residential spaces and both new construction and existing buildings as well as how to support other professionals working on LEED projects. *If you are a LEED AP without specialty or you have already earned the Green Associate credential, you need to take only Part 2 of the LEED AP BD+C exam. (Go to the Green Building Certification Institute [GBCI] website, www.gbci.org, for details.)* [1]

PART 2: A two-hour exam. Passing Part 2 attests that the individual possesses the knowledge and skills necessary to participate in the design process, to support and encourage integrated design, and to streamline the application and certification process.[2]

You must pass Part 1 before you can take Part 2. You may take both parts of the exam either on the same day or on separate days.

STEP 1:   **Read** the GBCI LEED AP Building Design + Construction Candidate Handbook at www.gbci.org to determine whether you meet the eligibility requirements.

STEP 2:   **Register** for and schedule your exam.

Tips: Register in the EXACT name that appears on your I.D. card, and keep your confirmation number.

STEP 3:   **Access** the appropriate reference documents.

The LEED® AP Building Design + Construction Candidate Handbook lists the references that are the sources for exam questions. Some references are available for free download at www.gbci.org, and others can be purchased at www.usgbc.org.

Note that exam reference documents are subject to change as the GBCI exams evolve. Always check the candidate handbooks for the most up-to-date list of reference documents.

Exam Part 1 (Green Associate):

Review the references listed in the LEED AP Building Design + Construction Candidate Handbook and consider purchasing the Green Building and LEED Core Concepts Guide from the U.S. Green Building Council (USGBC). This core resource is now packaged to include the Study Guide for LEED Green Associate!

1   *LEED AP Building Design + Construction Candidate Handbook* (GBCI, 2009)
2   *LEED AP Building Design + Construction Candidate Handbook* (GBCI, 2009)

Exam Part 2 (Building Design + Construction):

References: Examination items are developed from these resources.

- *LEED Reference Guide for Green Building Design & and Construction,* U.S. Green Building Council (available for purchase at www.usgbc.org/store > Publications);

- *Sustainable Building Technical Manual: Part II*, by Anthony Bernheim and William Reed, (1996);

- *Guidance on Innovation & Design (ID) Credits* (U.S. Green Building Council, 2004);

- *Guidelines for CIR Customers* (U.S. Green Building Council, 2007);

- *LEED Online v2 — Sample Credit Templates* (www.usgbc.org);

- *Cost of Green Revisited,* by Davis Langdon (2007); and

- *Energy Performance of LEED® for New Construction Buildings: Final Report,* by Cathy Turner and Mark Frankel (2008).

You should be familiar with the content of the U.S. Green Building Council's website, www.usgbc.org, and the Green Building Certification Institute's website, www.gbci.org, including, but not limited to, the various LEED rating systems, LEED checklists, LEED Project Registration, LEED Certification content, and the purpose of LEED Online.

STEP 4: **Start studying!**

Have all of the reference documents available as you work through this study guide, most importantly the LEED Reference Guide for Green Building Design and Construction.

LEED AP BUILDING DESIGN + CONSTRUCTION

ABOUT THE EXAM

I. Content Areas

The exam has seven major areas of focus, which are called out in the candidate handbook. Here is how they align with the Rating System credit categories:

GBCI EXAM AREAS OF FOCUS		LEED RATING SYSTEM CREDIT CATEGORIES
I. **Project Site Factors**	=	Sustainable Sites (SS)
II. **Water Management**	=	Water Efficiency (WE)
III. **Project Systems and Energy Impacts**	=	Energy and Atmosphere (EA)
IV. **Acquisition, Installation, and Management of Project Materials**	=	Materials and Resources (MR)
V. **Improvements to the Indoor Environment**	=	Indoor Environmental Quality (IEQ)
VI. **Stakeholder Involvement in Innovation**	=	**Innovation in Design (ID) & Regional Priority (RP)**
VII. **Project Surroundings and Public Outreach**	=	

GBCI exam questions are:

- Developed and validated by global work groups of subject matter experts;
- Referenced to current standards and resources;
- Developed and monitored through psychometric analysis; and
- Designed to satisfy the test development specifications of a job analysis.

The questions assess your knowledge at three levels:

- **Recall questions** test your direct knowledge of concepts. This section may require you to define terms or concepts, recall facts, recognize or identify components or steps in a process, and group items into categories.

- **Application questions** evaluate your knowledge of procedures and performance and may require you to demonstrate how things work, perform calculations following a formula, place components or steps into proper sequence, describe how a process works, and apply a known process or sequence of actions to accomplish a task (such as troubleshooting a problem using a detailed checklist).

- **Analysis questions** test your reasoning and problem-solving abilities. Such questions may require you to demonstrate an understanding of how things work, cause and effect, and underlying rationale; analyze problems and devise appropriate solutions; build a conceptual model of a process; and troubleshoot a problem without a checklist.

Questions follow consistent formats:

- You will likely **never** see an "all of the above," "none of the above," "true/false" or "what is the best?" type of question on this test, because:
    - These questions can cause confusion and have overlapping answers;
    - The test is intended to be clear and straightforward; and
    - The question language is never intended to be tricky.

- You will likely **never** see a credit number listed by itself; any direct reference to a LEED credit will include the full credit name.

- Most acronyms are spelled out so that you do not need to memorize all acronyms you learn.
    - Commonly referenced acronyms may be used (i.e. LEED, ASHRAE, and VOC), so it is still a good idea to know what these acronyms stand for!

- You **will** see some questions with multiple correct answers (for example, a question prompting the reader to "select two" responses).

- While this is not a math test, you **will** need to have a good understanding of the required calculations and equations associated with compliance to LEED prerequisites and credits. The Prometric center will have a built-in calculator on the computer screen for you to use during the exam. No outside calculators will be permitted.

PRACTICE QUESTIONS IN THIS STUDY GUIDE

Practice questions in this guide were written by subject matter experts who were trained by Prometric, which is the same testing company that administers the GBCI LEED exams, using the same guidelines as the item writers for the actual examinations. The practice questions in this guide will help you become familiar with the exam expectations, format, and question type. This should improve your testing skills and alleviate stress on test day, allowing you to focus on core information.

STUDY TIPS

You will learn best if you establish a regular study schedule over a period of time. Daily studying in shorter sessions is more effective for most people than "cramming" in long sessions at the last minute.

Studying with a partner or a group can help you stay on schedule and give you opportunities to quiz and drill with each other.

Here's a step-by-step approach for using your study resources:

- Read the corresponding section in this study guide.

- Take notes and highlight key points.

- Review other reference materials that apply to the category, such as referenced standards, resources listed in the LEED Reference Guide for Green Building Design and Construction, and other ancillary references listed in the LEED AP Building Design + Construction Candidate Handbook.

- Reread the reference guide categories.

- Use the review questions, learning activities, and practice questions in this guide.

- Continue reviewing and rereading until you are confident you know the material. Flash cards can also help instill confidence, through repetition.

- If there are subject areas with which you are unfamiliar, ask an expert in these areas to explain the concepts and subtopics to you.

EXAM DAY TIPS

General Strategies

- Always arrive early and take a moment to relax and reduce your anxiety.
  - This brief time period will boost your confidence.
  - Use this time to focus your mind and think positive thoughts.
- Plan how you will use the allotted time.
  - Estimate how many minutes you will need to finish each test section.
  - Determine a pace that will ensure that you complete the whole test on time.
  - Don't spend too much time on each question.
- Maintain a positive attitude.
  - Don't let more difficult questions raise your anxiety and steal your valuable time. Move on and find success with other questions.
  - Avoid watching for patterns. Noticing that the last four answers are "c" is not a good reason to stop, go back, and break concentration.
- Rely on your first impressions.
  - The answer that comes to mind first is often correct.
  - Nervously reviewing questions and changing answers can do more harm than good.
  - Use the "marked question" option to mark those questions you are certain that you want to reconsider.
- Plan to finish early and have time for review.
  - Return to difficult questions you marked for review.
  - Make sure you answered all questions.

Multiple Choice Strategies

- Formulate your own answer before reading the options.
  - Look away from the question and see whether you can answer it without looking at the choices. Focus on finding an answer without the help of the alternative options.
- Read all the choices before choosing your answer.
- Eliminate unlikely answers first.
  - Eliminating two alternatives quickly may increase your probability to 50-50 or better.
- Look for any factor that will make a statement false.

- It is easy for the examiner to add a false part to an otherwise true statement.
- Test takers often read the question and see some truth and quickly assume that the entire statement is true. For example, "Water boils at 212 degrees in Denver." Water does boil at 212 degrees, but not at Denver's altitude.

- Beware that similar answers provide a clue. One of them is correct; the others are disguised.

  - This is likely not a trick, but make sure you know the exact content being asked.

- Consider the answers carefully. If more than one answer seems correct for a single-answer question:

  - Ask yourself whether the answer you're considering completely addresses the question.
  - If the answer is only partly true or is true only under certain narrow conditions, it's probably not the right answer.
  - If you have to make a significant assumption in order for the answer to be true, ask yourself whether this assumption is obvious enough that everyone would make it. If it is not, ignore that answer.

- If you suspect that a question is a trick question, make sure you're not reading too much into the question, and try to avoid imagining detailed scenarios in which the answer could be true. In most cases, "trick questions" are only tricky because they're not taken at face value.

  - The test questions will include only relevant content and are not intended to trick you or test your reading ability.

BUILDING DESIGN + CONSTRUCTION

THE RUNDOWN

Green Building Design + Construction includes the LEED for New Construction, LEED for Core & Shell, and LEED for Schools rating systems. These are a set of performance standards for certifying the design and construction of commercial or institutional buildings and high-rise residential buildings of all sizes, both public and private. The intent is to promote healthful, durable, affordable, and environmentally sound practices in building design and construction.

NC

	SS	WE	EA	MR	IEQ	ID	RP	Total
Prerequisites	1	1	3	1	2	-	-	8
Credits	14	3	6	8	15	2	1	49
Possible Points	26	10	35	14	15	6	4	110

Schools

	SS	WE	EA	MR	IEQ	ID	RP	Total
Prerequisites	2	1	3	1	3	-	-	10
Credits	16	4	6	8	19	3	1	57
Possible Points	24	11	33	13	23	6	4	114

CS

	SS	WE	EA	MR	IEQ	ID	RP	Total
Prerequisites	1	1	3	1	2	-	-	8
Credits	15	3	7	6	12	2	1	46
Possible Points	28	10	37	13	12	6	4	110

Rating System	Reference Guide
LEED for New Construction and Major Renovations	The LEED 2009 Reference Guide for Green Building Design and Construction
LEED for Core & Shell	
LEED for Schools	

Although the LEED for New Construction, LEED for Core & Shell, and LEED for Schools rating systems have many similarities, they are each unique to specific project types and should be implemented accordingly.

LEED for New Construction and Major Renovations: All commercial buildings as defined by standard building codes are eligible. This rating system addresses design and construction activities for new buildings and major renovations. The owner or tenant must occupy more than 50% of the building's leasable square footage.

LEED for Core & Shell: Projects in which the developer controls the design and construction of the entire core and shell base building, but not the tenant fit-out, are eligible. The owner or tenant must occupy 50% or less of the building's leasable square footage.

LEED for Schools: This system encompasses design and construction activities for new schools and major renovations of existing schools. The project must be an academic building on K–12 school grounds. Postsecondary academic buildings or prekindergarten buildings can choose to apply for either LEED for New Construction or LEED for Schools certification.

In order for a building to be certified, it must satisfy all the prerequisites and accumulate enough points to earn the desired project rating under LEED for New Construction, Core & Shell, or Schools. Building certification is validated through a formal third-party review process administered through GBCI.

LEED for Core & Shell has a unique and voluntary precertification option. Precertification offers building owners and developers a marketing tool to help attract potential tenants and financiers. To achieve precertification, the project team completes an initial review process in which GBCI reviews a summary of early design stage submittal material. This material, which reflects a studied and realistic set of project goals and intentions, forms the basis for the awarding of precertification. Projects that earn precertification must complete all of the typically required documentation to earn formal LEED Core & Shell certification.

THE PROCESS AND PLAYERS

Prior to addressing any LEED-specific prerequisites or credits, it is important to establish common ground and set targeted sustainability goals with the entire project team. This step, commonly referred to as a goal-setting charrette, should ideally take place as early in the design process as possible. Goals for the charrette may follow the *Environmental Design Guidelines described in the Sustainable Building Technical Manual: Part II,* by Anthony Bernheim and William Reed (1996):

- Establish a vision statement that embraces sustainable principles and an integrated design approach.
- Establish the project's green building goals, developed from the vision statement.
- Establish green design criteria.
- Set priorities for the project design criteria.

Once the goals and criteria are established, it is critical to understand the phases and tasks involved in the LEED certification process.

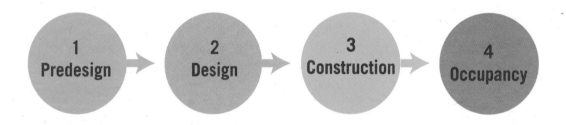

TIME LINE AND TEAM

Achieving LEED certification requires the involvement of the right project team members in each project phase and task.

A time line/team graphic can be found on each credit page that identifies the primary phase and responsible party or parties associated with that prerequisite or credit.

The key phases are as follows:

- Predesign;
- Design;
- Construction; and
- Occupancy.

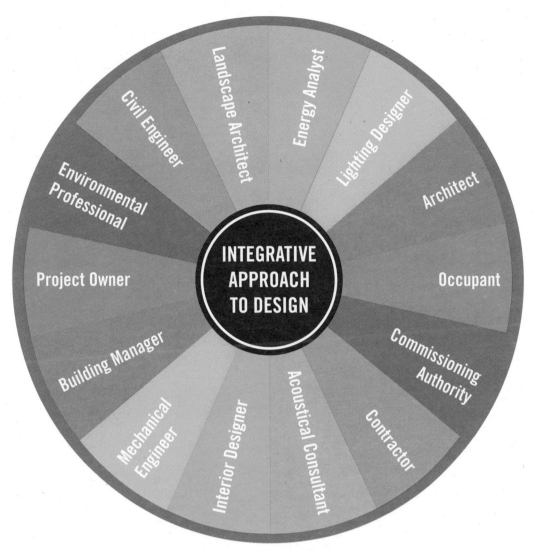

The diagram shows an "INTEGRATIVE APPROACH TO DESIGN" wheel with the following segments: Landscape Architect, Energy Analyst, Lighting Designer, Architect, Occupant, Commissioning Authority, Contractor, Acoustical Consultant, Interior Designer, Mechanical Engineer, Building Manager, Project Owner, Environmental Professional, Civil Engineer.

The key players are the following:

- Project owner;
- Occupant;
- Building manager;
- Architect;
- Mechanical engineer;
- Lighting designer;
- Contractor;

- Civil engineer;
- Landscape architect;
- Interior designer;
- Energy analyst;
- Commissioning authority;
- Environmental professional; and
- Acoustical consultant.

An integrative, multidisciplinary approach allows experts to share their knowledge and successfully coordinate individual design efforts to achieve a well-functioning, environmentally responsible, integrated building.[3]

3 *Sustainable Building Technical Manual: Part II*, by Anthony Bernheim and William Reed, (1996)

THE OTHER PARTICULARS

There are other basic elements involved in LEED for New Construction, Core & Shell, and Schools certification that aren't addressed in any one specific credit, but are integral to the entire rating system. These include the following:

Minimum Program Requirements (MPRs):

Pretty plain and simple - if a project doesn't meet the MPRs, it's not eligible for LEED certification. And, if GBCI learns of non-compliance to the MPRs sometime down the road, they can revoke your LEED certification at any time. Bottom line, become familiar with these basic project requirements and know that they determine project eligibility for LEED. The MPRs will evolve over time and can be found published on the USGBC website at http://www.usgbc.org/DisplayPage.aspx?CMSPageID=2014.

General Submittal Requirements:

The General Submittal Template asks for basic building information and must be completed and uploaded to LEED Online. This template, which also requires the uploading of basic building documents, drawings, and plans, must be consistent across all submitted documentation.

Full-Time Equivalent (FTE):

It is important to establish the occupancy demands on a project early, because this number will affect the approach taken on some LEED prerequisites and credits and should be used consistently in LEED documentation. Calculate the FTE for both full-time and part-time employees, assuming that an 8-hour occupant has an FTE value of 1.0; part-time occupants have an FTE value based on their hours per day divided by the standard occupancy period (typically 8 hours).

Equation: FTE Occupants = Occupant Hours/8

Core & Shell projects have default occupancy figures that must be used when final occupancy counts are not available. For details, refer to the LEED Reference Guide for Green Building Design and Construction, Core & Shell Appendix 1.

Credit Interpretation Requests and Rulings (CIRs):

CIRs were established for project applicants seeking technical and administrative guidance on how LEED credits apply to their projects and vice versa. It is important for project teams to be aware of previous CIRs, as the project must adhere to the CIRs current at the time of registration in addition to the ruling received for their own CIRs. CIRs must be formally submitted online.

Here's what you need to know about CIRs:

- Do your homework! Critically review the intent of the credit/prerequisite and determine whether you are meeting that intent. Consult all available resources, such as the LEED reference guide and previous CIRs, and contact a LEED customer service representative to confirm that your situation warrants a new CIR.

- Properly submit your CIR! Do not include unnecessary or confidential information; provide only what is essential. Request guidance on only one credit or prerequisite, with pertinent background information limited to 600 words. No attachments are accepted!

- There is no guarantee! CIRs do not guarantee a credit award, and you will still have to demonstrate and document achievement during the certification process.

NOTES...

SUSTAINABLE SITES

The project site quite literally and figuratively serves as the foundation for green buildings. Buildings do not exist in a vacuum; they are living parts of a larger fabric, each within its own unique context. The Sustainable Sites (SS) category focuses on selecting sites that reduce dependency on automobiles, incorporating strategies that enhance plant and wildlife habitats, and maintaining water and air quality.

WHAT ABOUT SUSTAINABLE SITES?

How can a building encourage occupants to ride their bikes or use public transportation?

What strategies would enhance nighttime security without adding additional lighting?

How can agricultural land, parks, and wildlife refuges be protected?

What environmental implications are associated with the heat island effect? Is the heat island effect a consideration only in urban areas?

Photo courtesy of Green Building Services

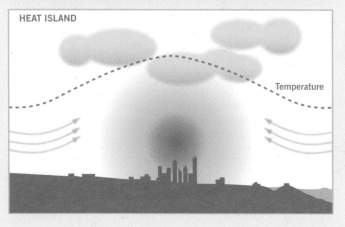

HEAT ISLAND

Temperature

SUSTAINABLE SITES

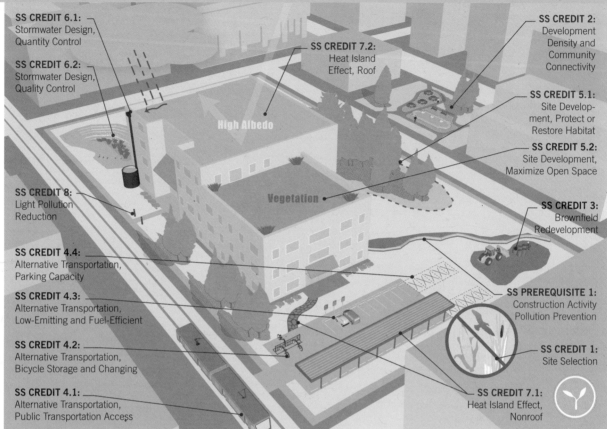

SS CREDIT 6.1: Stormwater Design, Quantity Control

SS CREDIT 6.2: Stormwater Design, Quality Control

SS CREDIT 8: Light Pollution Reduction

SS CREDIT 4.4: Alternative Transportation, Parking Capacity

SS CREDIT 4.3: Alternative Transportation, Low-Emitting and Fuel-Efficient

SS CREDIT 4.2: Alternative Transportation, Bicycle Storage and Changing

SS CREDIT 4.1: Alternative Transportation, Public Transportation Access

SS CREDIT 7.2: Heat Island Effect, Roof

High Albedo

Vegetation

SS CREDIT 2: Development Density and Community Connectivity

SS CREDIT 5.1: Site Development, Protect or Restore Habitat

SS CREDIT 5.2: Site Development, Maximize Open Space

SS CREDIT 3: Brownfield Redevelopment

SS PREREQUISITE 1: Construction Activity Pollution Prevention

SS CREDIT 1: Site Selection

SS CREDIT 7.1: Heat Island Effect, Nonroof

OVERVIEW

LEED strategies in the Sustainable Sites category address environmental concerns related to building location, site conditions, hardscape areas, and other exterior features. The category promotes the following measures:

- Selecting and developing the site wisely;
- Reducing emissions associated with transportation;
- Protecting surrounding habitats;
- Providing and maintaining open space;
- Managing stormwater runoff;
- Reducing the heat island effect; and
- Eliminating light pollution.

SUSTAINABLE SITES

Selecting a project site and developing the site with sustainable practices is a key element of green building. Site selection will affect the environmental footprint of a building long after the construction crew has left the job. The site's location will influence how people travel to it—do they drive in their cars alone, grab a bus, or hop on their bikes? Once a site is chosen, there are numerous strategies a project team can integrate to minimize environmental harm from development. For instance, engineers can design stormwater systems that mimic the natural environment and create a site layout that preserves environmentally sensitive areas.

SYNERGIES

The Sustainable Sites category has synergies with almost all of the other Building Design and Construction categories because a project's location and site development are so intrinsic to the building's ultimate function. One of the most recognizable connections is that between the stormwater design and water efficiency. Landscapes that utilize drought-tolerant and -adapted plants not only help slow and filter stormwater, but also reduce the need for irrigation—one of the largest uses of water in buildings. Additionally, site development strategies interact with each other. A site with appropriate vegetative features will allow for the allocation of green spaces, as well as assist in stormwater retention and a reduction in the urban heat island effect. Also, think about how the building's orientation can affect its energy performance or how selecting a site with ample access to natural resources might influence how far materials have to travel to get to the site.

CATEGORY HIGHLIGHTS

- There is one prerequisite in this category for New Construction and Core & Shell projects. Schools projects have a second prerequisite.

- The Sustainable Sites category is second in total possible points, after the Energy and Atmosphere category. New Construction projects have 26 possible points in this category, Schools projects have 24, and Core & Shell projects have 28.

- Five of the credits in this category allow points for exemplary performance. Schools projects have an additional exemplary performance credit available.

- You will need to know the full-time equivalent (FTE) occupancy for the project in order to complete calculations for several of the credits. This measure considers all the building users and how much time in total they are in the building. The FTE needs to be used consistently across all credits.

SUSTAINABLE SITES CREDITS

SUSTAINABLE SITE CREDITS

CREDIT	TITLE	NC	SCHOOL	CS
SS Prerequisite 1	Construction Activity Pollution Prevention	Required	Required	Required
SS Prerequisite 2	Environmental Site Assessment	N/A	Required	N/A
SS Credit 1	Site Selection	1 point	1 point	1 point
SS Credit 2	Development Density and Community Connectivity	5 points	4 points	5 points
SS Credit 3	Brownfield Redevelopment	1 point	1 point	1 point
SS Credit 4.1	Alternative Transportation— Public Transportation Access	6 points	4 points	6 points
SS Credit 4.2	Alternative Transportation— Bicycle Storage and Changing Rooms	1 point	1 point	2 points
SS Credit 4.3	Alternative Transportation— Low-Emitting and Fuel-Efficient Vehicles	3 points	2 points	3 points
SS Credit 4.4	Alternative Transportation— Parking Capacity	2 points	2 points	2 points
SS Credit 5.1	Site Development— Protect or Restore Habitat	1 point	1 point	1 point
SS Credit 5.2	Site Development— Maximize Open Space	1 point	1 point	1 point
SS Credit 6.1	Stormwater Design— Quantity Control	1 point	1 point	1 point
SS Credit 6.2	Stormwater Design— Quality Control	1 point	1 point	1 point
SS Credit 7.1	Heat Island Effect— Nonroof	1 point	1 point	1 point
SS Credit 7.2	Heat Island Effect— Roof	1 point	1 point	1 point
SS Credit 8	Light Pollution Reduction	1 point	1 point	1 point
SS Credit 9	Tenant Design and Construction Guidelines	N/A	N/A	1 point
SS Credit 9	Site Master Plan	N/A	1 point	N/A
SS Credit 10	Joint Use of Facilities	N/A	1 point	N/A

KEY TERMS

Adapted (or introduced) plants	These plants reliably grow well in a given habitat with minimal winter protection, pest control, fertilization, or irrigation once their root systems are established. Adapted plants are considered low maintenance and not invasive.
Albedo	See solar reflectance.
Alternative fuel vehicles	Vehicles that use low-polluting, nongasoline fuels such as electricity, hydrogen, propane, compressed natural gas, liquid natural gas, methanol, and ethanol. In LEED, efficient gas–electric hybrid vehicles are included in this group.
Aquifer	An underground water-bearing rock formation or group of formations that supply groundwater, wells, or springs.
Area-weighted SRI	A weighted average calculation that may be performed for buildings with multiple roof surfaces to demonstrate that the total roof area has an average solar reflectance index equal to or greater than that of a theoretical roof 75% of whose surfaces have an SRI of 78 and 25% have an SRI of 30.
Attendance boundary	Used by school districts to determine which students attend what school based on where they live.
Biodiversity	The variety of life in all forms, levels, and combinations, including ecosystem diversity, species diversity, and genetic diversity.
Brownfield	Real property whose use may be complicated by the presence or possible presence of a hazardous substance, pollutant, or contaminant.
Building density	The floor area of the building divided by the total area of the site (square feet per acre).
Building footprint	The area on a project site used by the building structure, defined by the perimeter of the building plan. Parking lots, landscapes, and other nonbuilding facilities are not included in the building footprint.
Campus or private bus	A bus or shuttle service that is privately operated and not available to the general public. In LEED, a campus or private bus line that operates within 1/4 mile of the project site and provides transportation service to the public can contribute to earning credits.
Carpool	An arrangement by which two or more people share a vehicle for transportation.

Comprehensive Environmental Response, Compensation and Liability Act, or CERCLA	CERCLA is more commonly known as Superfund. Enacted in 1980, CERCLA addresses abandoned or historical waste sites and contamination by taxing the chemical and petroleum industries and providing federal authority to respond to releases of hazardous substances.
Curfew hours	Locally determined times when lighting restrictions are imposed. When no local or regional restrictions are in place, 10:00 p.m. is regarded as a default curfew time.
Development footprint	The area affected by development or by project site activity. Hardscape, access roads, parking lots, nonbuilding facilities, and the building itself are all included in the development footprint.
Ecosystem	A basic unit of nature that includes a community of organisms and their nonliving environment linked by biological, chemical, and physical processes.
Emissivity	The ratio of the radiation emitted by a surface to the radiation emitted by a black body at the same temperature.
Endangered species	Threatened with extinction because of harmful human activities or environmental factors.
Erosion	A combination of processes or events by which materials of the earth's surface are loosened, dissolved, or worn away and transported by natural agents (such as water, wind, or gravity).
Eutrophication	The increase in chemical nutrients, such as the nitrogen and phosphorus often found in fertilizers, in an ecosystem. The added nutrients stimulate excessive plant growth, promoting algal blooms or weeds. The enhanced plant growth reduces oxygen in the land and water, reducing water quality and fish and other animal populations.
Footcandle (fc)	A measure of light falling on a given surface. One footcandle is defined as the quantity of light falling on a 1 square-foot area from a 1 candela light source at a distance of 1 foot (which equals 1 lumen per square foot). Footcandles can be measured both horizontally and vertically by a footcandle meter or light meter.
Fuel-efficient vehicles	Vehicles that have achieved a minimum green score of 40 according to the annual vehicle rating guide of the American Council for an Energy Efficient Economy.
Full cut-off luminaire	A luminaire that has zero candela intensity at an angle of 90 degrees above the vertical axis (nadir or straight down) and at all angles greater than 90 degrees from straight down. Additionally, the candela per 1,000 lamp lumens does not numerically exceed 100 (10%) at an angle of 80 degrees above nadir. This applies to all lateral angles around the luminaire.

Full-time equivalent (FTE)	Represents a regular building occupant who spends 40 hours per week in the project building. Part-time or overtime occupants have FTE values based on their hours per week divided by 40. Multiple shifts are included or excluded depending on the intent and requirements of the credit.
Greenfields	Sites not previously developed or graded that could support open space, habitat, or agriculture.
Greenhouse gases (GHGs)	These absorb and emit radiation at specific wavelengths within the spectrum of thermal infrared radiation emitted by the earth's surface, clouds, and the atmosphere itself. Increased concentrations of greenhouse gases are a root cause of global climate change.
Hardscape	The inanimate elements of the building landscaping. Examples include pavement, roadways, stone walls, concrete paths and sidewalks, and concrete, brick, and tile patios.
Heat island effect	The absorption of heat by hardscapes, such as dark, nonreflective pavement and buildings, and its radiation to surrounding areas. Particularly in urban areas, other sources may include vehicle exhaust, air conditioners, and street equipment; reduced airflow from tall buildings and narrow streets exacerbates the effect.
Horizontal footcandles	Horizontal footcandles occur on a horizontal surface. They can be added together arithmetically when more than one source provides light to the same surface.
Hybrid vehicles	Vehicles that use a gasoline engine to drive an electric generator and use the electric generator and/or storage batteries to power electric motors that drive the vehicle's wheels.
Hydrology	The study of water occurrence, distribution, movement, and balances in an ecosystem.
Impervious surfaces	Surfaces with a perviousness of less than 50% and promote runoff of water instead of infiltration into the subsurface. Examples include parking lots, roads, sidewalks, and plazas.
In situ remediation	Treatment of contaminants using technologies such as injection wells or reactive trenches. These methods employ the natural hydraulic gradient of groundwater and usually require only minimal disturbance of the site.

Infrared (or thermal) emittance	A parameter between 0 and 1 (or 0% and 100%) that indicates the ability of a material to shed infrared radiation (heat). The wavelength range for this radiant energy is roughly 5 to 40 micrometers. Most building materials (including glass) are opaque in this part of the spectrum and have an emittance of roughly 0.9. Materials such as clean, bare metals are the most important exceptions to the 0.9 rule. Thus, clean, untarnished galvanized steel has low emittance, and aluminum roof coatings have intermediate emittance levels.
Invasive plants	Invasive plants are nonnative to the ecosystem and likely to cause harm once introduced. These species are characteristically adaptable and aggressive, have a high reproductive capacity, and tend to overrun the ecosystems they enter. Collectively, they are among the greatest threats to biodiversity and ecosystem stability.
Light pollution	Waste light from building sites that produces glare, is directed upward to the sky, or is directed off the site. Waste light does not increase nighttime safety, utility, or security and needlessly consumes energy.
Light trespass	Light that is obtrusive and unwanted because of quantitative, directional, or spectral attributes. Light trespass can cause annoyance, discomfort, distraction, or loss of visibility.
Local zoning requirements	Local government regulations imposed to promote orderly development of private lands and prevent land-use conflicts.
Low-emitting vehicles	Vehicles that are classified as zero-emission vehicles (ZEVs) by the California Air Resources Board.
Mass transit	Transportation designed to transport large groups of persons in a single vehicle, such as a bus or train.
Master plan	In LEED, the master plan is an overall design or development concept for the school and associated buildings and site. This concept considers future use, growth, and contraction and includes ways to manage the facility and sustainable features. The master plan is typically illustrated with narrative descriptions, building plans, and site drawings of phases and planned development.
Mixed use	Mixed-use projects involve a combination of residential and commercial or retail components.
National Pollutant Discharge Elimination System (NPDES)	A permit program that controls water pollution by regulating point sources that discharge pollutants into waters of the United States. Industrial, municipal, and other facilities must obtain permits if their discharges go directly to surface waters.

Native (or indigenous) plants	Plants that are adapted to a given area during a defined time period and are not invasive. In North America, the term often refers to plants growing in a region prior to the time of settlement by people of European descent.
Open spaces	Open space areas are typically defined by local zoning requirements. If local zoning requirements do not clearly define open space, it is defined for the purposes of LEED calculations as the property area minus the development footprint; it must be vegetated and pervious, with exceptions only as noted in the credit requirements section. Only ground areas are calculated as open space. For projects located in urban areas that earn a Development Density and Community Connectivity credit, open space also includes nonvehicular, pedestrian-oriented hardscape spaces.
Open-grid pavement	Pavement that is less than 50% impervious and accommodates vegetation in the open cells.
Perviousness	The percentage of the surface area of a paving system that is open and allows moisture to soak into the ground below.
Preferred parking	Parking that is available to particular users and includes designated spaces close to the building (aside from designated handicapped spots), designated covered spaces, discounted parking passes, and guaranteed passes in a lottery system.
Previously developed sites	Sites that already have buildings, roadways, and parking lots or were graded or otherwise altered by direct human activities.
Property area	The total area within the legal property boundaries of a site; it encompasses all areas of the site, including constructed and nonconstructed areas.
Public transportation	Bus, rail, or other transit services for the general public that operate on a regular, continual basis.
Remediation	The process of cleaning up a contaminated site by physical, chemical, or biological means. Remediation processes are typically applied to contaminated soil and groundwater.
Residential area	Land zoned primarily for housing at a density of 10 units per acre or greater. These areas may have single-family and multifamily housing and include building types such as townhomes, apartments, duplexes, condominiums, or mobile homes.

Resource Conservation and Recovery Act (RCRA)	An EPA-established act that addresses active and future facilities and was enacted in 1976 to give the EPA authority to control hazardous wastes from cradle to grave, including generation, transportation, treatment, storage, and disposal. Some nonhazardous wastes are also covered under RCRA.
Retention ponds	Ponds that capture stormwater runoff and clear it of pollutants before its release. Some retention pond designs use gravity only; others use mechanical equipment, such as pipes and pumps, to facilitate transport. Some ponds are dry except during storm events; others permanently store water.
Safety and comfort light levels	Light levels that are local code requirements and must be adequate to provide a safe path for egress without over lighting the area.
Sedimentation	The addition of soil particles to water bodies by natural and human-related activities. Sedimentation often decreases water quality and can accelerate the aging process of lakes, rivers, and streams.
Shielding	A nontechnical term that describes devices or techniques that are used as part of a luminaire or lamp to limit glare, light trespass, or sky glow.
Site area	See property area.
Site assessment	An evaluation of a site's aboveground and subsurface characteristics, including its structures, geology, and hydrology. Site assessments are typically used to determine whether contamination has occurred, as well as the extent and concentration of any release of pollutants. Information generated during a site assessment is used to make remedial action decisions.
Sky glow	Sky glow is caused by stray light from unshielded light sources and light reflecting off surfaces that then enters the atmosphere and illuminates and reflects off dust, debris, and water vapor. Sky glow can substantially limit observation of the night sky, compromise astronomical research, and harm nocturnal environments.
Solar reflectance, or albedo	A measure of the ability of a surface material to reflect sunlight—visible, infrared, and ultraviolet wavelengths—on a scale of 0 to 1. Black paint has a solar reflectance of 0; white paint (titanium dioxide) has a solar reflectance of 1.

Solar reflectance index (SRI)	A measure of a material's ability to reject solar heat, as shown by a small temperature rise. Standard black (reflectance 0.05, emittance 0.90) is 0 and standard white (reflectance 0.80, emittance 0.90) is 100. For example, a standard black surface has a temperature rise of 90 F (50 C) in full sun, and a standard white surface has a temperature rise of 14.6 F (8.1 C). Once the maximum temperature rise of a given material has been computed, the SRI can be calculated by interpolating between the values for white and black. Materials with the highest SRI values are the coolest choices for paving. Because of the way SRI is defined, particularly hot materials can even take slightly negative values, and particularly cool materials can even exceed 100. (Lawrence Berkeley National Laboratory Cool Roofing Materials Database)
Stormwater pollution prevention plan	This plan includes all measures planned to prevent stormwater contamination, control sedimentation and erosion during construction, and comply with the requirements of the Clean Water Act.
Stormwater runoff	Water from precipitation that flows over surfaces into sewer systems or receiving water bodies. All precipitation that leaves project site boundaries on the surface is considered stormwater runoff.
Total suspended solids (TSS)	Particles that are too small or light to be removed from stormwater via gravity settling. Suspended solid concentrations are typically removed via filtration.
Transient users	Occupants who do not use a facility on a consistent, regular, daily basis. Examples include students in higher education settings, customers in retail settings, and visitors in institutional settings.
Vertical footcandles	Footcandles that occur on a vertical surface. They can be added together arithmetically when more than one source provides light to the same surface.

KEY TERMS

EROSION

SEDIMENTATION

STORMWATER POLLUTION PREVENTION PLAN

STORMWATER RUNOFF

RELATED CREDITS

 SS Credit 5.1: Site Development – Protect or Restore Habitat

 SS Credit 5.2: Site Development – Maximize Open Space

 SS Credit 6.1: Stormwater Design – Quantity Control

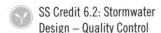 SS Credit 6.2: Stormwater Design – Quality Control

INTENT

To reduce pollution from construction activities by controlling soil erosion, waterway sedimentation, and airborne dust generation.

REQUIREMENTS

Implement an erosion and sedimentation control plan during construction that prevents the loss of soil from stormwater runoff and/or wind erosion, the sedimentation of storm sewers or receiving streams, and pollution from particulates in the air.

IMPLEMENTATION

- Under natural conditions, vegetation holds soil in place. Construction activities, including excavation, grading, equipment operation, and even foot traffic, result in soil loss and water quality issues. An Erosion and Sedimentation Control (ESC) Plan ensures that measures are put into place to minimize the negative impacts of construction activities on a site.

- Typical measures in an ESC plan include stabilization measures and structural controls. Stabilization measures include planting grasses and shrubs to stabilize the soil, using mulch to cover and hold soils. Structural controls include installing silt fencing, building earth dikes, and constructing an area on-site to trap sediments.

- Educate subcontractors about the ESC plan so that measures are employed consistently.

- Review the site daily and weekly to ensure that the ESC measures are being implemented properly. Correct any issues as they arise.

DOCUMENTATION & CALCULATIONS

- Develop an erosion and sedimentation control drawing and/or a written ESC plan with specifications that detail the erosion and control best management practices used on the project site and the responsible parties for implementation.

- Over the course of site work activities, document implementation of the ESC plan through date-stamped photos, inspection logs or reports, descriptions of corrective actions in response to problems, and the like.

NOTES

None

TIME LINE/TEAM

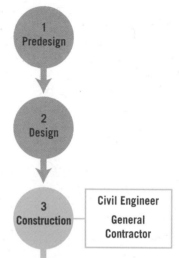

1 Predesign

2 Design

3 Construction — Civil Engineer / General Contractor

4 Occupancy

STANDARDS

2003 EPA Construction General Permit

KEY TERMS

BROWNFIELD

IN SITU REMEDIATION

REMEDIATION

SITE ASSESSMENT

RELATED CREDITS

 SS Credit 3: Brownfield
Redevelopment

INTENT

To ensure that the site is assessed for environmental contamination and, if contaminated, that the environmental contamination has been remediated to protect children's health.

REQUIREMENTS

Conduct a Phase I Environmental Site Assessment to determine whether environmental contamination exists on-site. If contamination is found, conduct a Phase II Environmental Site Assessment and associated remediation.

IMPLEMENTATION

- Conduct a Phase I Environmental Site Assessment. This type of assessment does not include any physical tests but relies instead on historical data, site visits, and interviews to identify whether a site may be contaminated.

- If there is reason to believe the site may be contaminated, a Phase II Environmental Site Assessment must be conducted. This level of inspection will include collection and analysis of samples from the site.

- Remediation will depend on what is discovered in the assessment: EPA Region 9 cleanup standards provide guidelines for the most appropriate cleanup measures.

SS Prerequisite 2:
Environmental Site Assessment (Schools)

Exemplary Performance

DOCUMENTATION & CALCULATIONS

Provide a Phase I Environmental Site Assessment and, if required, a Phase II assessment, detailing the contamination and documentation from the governing authority demonstrating that safe contamination levels have been reached.

NOTES

Land that was once a landfill is not eligible for LEED Schools certification.

TIME LINE/TEAM

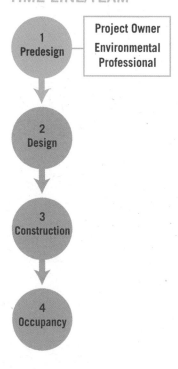

STANDARDS

ASTM E1527-05, Phase I Environmental Site Assessment

ASTM E1903-97, Phase II Environmental Site Assessment, effective 2002

Sustainable Sites   **31**

SS Credit 1:
Site Selection

KEY TERMS

ENDANGERED SPECIES

PREVIOUSLY DEVELOPED SITES

RELATED CREDITS

SS Credit 2: Development Density and Community Connectivity

SS Credit 3: Brownfield Redevelopment

SS Credit 4.1: Alternative Transportation – Public Transportation Access

SS Credit 5.1: Site Development – Protect or Restore Habitat

SS Credit 5.2: Site Development – Maximize Open Space

SS Credit 6.1: Stormwater Design – Quantity Control

SS Credit 6.2: Stormwater Design – Quality Control

INTENT

To avoid the development of inappropriate sites and reduce the environmental impact from the location of a building on a site.

REQUIREMENTS

Do not build on sites with the following conditions:

- Prime farmland;

- land within threatened or endangered species habitats;

- land near classified wetlands;

- land that is public parkland; or

- previously undeveloped land near a body of water or in a floodplain.

IMPLEMENTATION

- Create a list of potential sites, surveying their attributes against the restricted criteria.

- Chose an appropriate site to reduce the impact of development and preserve ecologically sensitive areas to allow the natural habitat and wildlife to thrive.

- Consider how to incorporate the natural design of the site with complementary functions.

DOCUMENTATION & CALCULATIONS

Provide narratives describing any special circumstances if any of the prohibited criteria have been violated, indicating how the intent of the credit has still been met.

NOTES

None

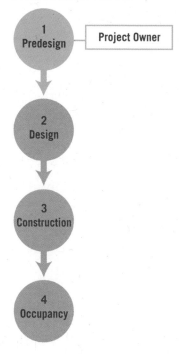

TIME LINE/TEAM

1
Predesign — Project Owner

2
Design

3
Construction

4
Occupancy

STANDARDS

U.S. Department of Agriculture, Definition of Prime Agricultural Land

Federal Emergency Management Agency, Definition of 100-Year Flood

Endangered Species Lists

National Marine Fisheries Service, List of Endangered Marine Species

United States Code of Federal Regulations, Definition of Wetlands

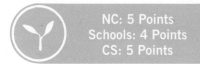

NC: 5 Points
Schools: 4 Points
CS: 5 Points

SS Credit 2:
Development Density and Community Connectivity

KEY TERMS

BUILDING DENSITY

GREENFIELDS

MIXED USE

PROPERTY AREA

SITE AREA

RELATED CREDITS

 SS Credit 1: Site Selection

 SS Credit 4.1: Alternative Transportation – Public Transportation Access

INTENT

To channel development to urban areas with existing infrastructure, protect greenfields, and preserve habitat and natural resources.

REQUIREMENTS

Build on previously developed land and meet either Option 1 or Option 2.

Option 1:
Build in an existing neighborhood with a density of 60,000 square feet per acre.
Exemplary Performance: Double the project's density compared with the average density within the calculated area.
Option 2:
Build within ½ mile of a residential area or a neighborhood with an average density of 10 units per acre, AND within ½ mile of 10 basic services, AND with pedestrian access between the building and the services.
Exemplary Performance: Select a site where the average density of the surrounding area is double the credit requirement (120,000 square feet per acre).

IMPLEMENTATION

- Select a site within a developed neighborhood to curb urban sprawl. Focus development in areas with existing infrastructure such as water lines, streets, and power. Additionally, focus selection on sites that provide opportunities to walk, bike, or take public transportation and that have basic services within walking distance.

- Meet or exceed local density goals.

DOCUMENTATION & CALCULATIONS

- For development density, calculate the development density using the equation below.

Equation 1 from the LEED Reference Guide for Green Building Design and Construction, 2009. Page 28. Development Density.

$$\text{Development Density (sf/acre)} = \frac{\text{Gross Building Area (sf)}}{\text{Site Area (acres)}}$$

Equation 2 from the LEED Reference Guide for Green Building Design and Construction, 2009. Page 29. Density Radius.

$$\text{Density Radius (lf)} = 3 \times \sqrt{\left[\text{Site Area (acres)} \times 43{,}560 \text{ (sf/acre)}\right]}$$

Equation 3 from the LEED Reference Guide for Green Building Design and Construction, 2009. Page 29. Average Property Density within Density Boundary.

$$\text{Average Property Density within Density Boundary} = \frac{\Sigma \text{ Square Footage}}{\Sigma \text{ Site Area}}$$

- For community connectivity projects, create a site vicinity plan that highlights the ½-mile radius and locations and types of qualifying services, as well as the location of residential areas.

Figure 1 from the LEED Reference Guide for Green Building Design and Construction, 2009. Page 27. Sample Map for Community Connectivity.

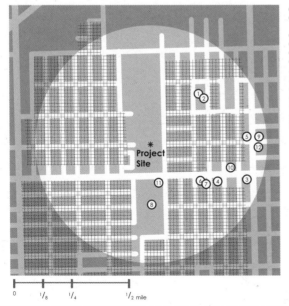

TIME LINE/TEAM

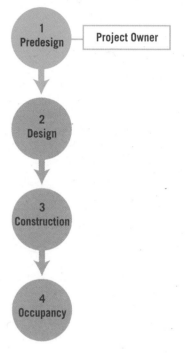

1 Predesign — Project Owner
2 Design
3 Construction
4 Occupancy

STANDARDS

None

NOTES

No fewer than 8 of the 10 services must be existing, operational businesses. Anticipated services must demonstrate they will be operational within 12 months of the project opening.

The only basic service that can be counted more than once is restaurants—two may be used.

Mixed-used projects may only use one service within the project boundary.

Schools are allowed to exclude project physical education spaces from the development density calculations.

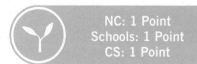

KEY TERMS

BROWNFIELD

IN SITU REMEDIATION

REMEDIATION

SITE ASSESSMENT

RELATED CREDITS

 SS Credit 1: Site Selection

 Schools SS Prerequisite 2:
Environmental Site Assessment

INTENT

To rehabilitate damaged sites where development is complicated by environmental contamination and to reduce pressure on undeveloped land.

REQUIREMENTS

Option 1:
Develop on a site documented as contaminated by means of an ASTM E1903-97 Phase II Environmental Site Assessment.
Option 2:
Develop on a site defined as a brownfield by a local, state, or federal government agency.

IMPLEMENTATION

- Conduct a Phase II Environmental Site Assessment or select a site that has been defined as a brownfield by a government agency.

- Develop a plan for remediation that considers both cost and environmental issues.

- Complete remediation efforts and continue to monitor the site to ensure that contamination problems do not recur.

DOCUMENTATION & CALCULATIONS

Provide a Phase II Environmental Site Assessment detailing the contamination and events surrounding the remediation.

NOTES

Schools can achieve this point only via SS Prerequisite 2: Environmental Site Assessment and by remediating the site contamination.

TIME LINE/TEAM

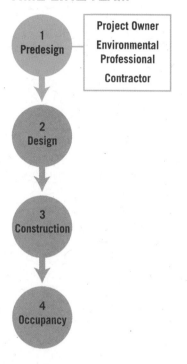

1 Predesign — Project Owner, Environmental Professional, Contractor

2 Design

3 Construction

4 Occupancy

STANDARDS

U.S. EPA, Definition of Brownfield

ASTM E1527-05, Phase I Environmental Site Assessment

ASTM E1903-97, Phase II Environmental Site Assessment, effective 2002

SS Credit 4.1: Alternative Transportation, Public Transportation Access

ATTENDANCE BOUNDARY

MASS TRANSIT

 SS Credit 1: Site Selection

 SS Credit 2: Development Density and Community Connectivity

INTENT

To reduce pollution and land development impacts from automobile use.

REQUIREMENTS

Provide dedicated pedestrian access to off-site transit lines for all of the options below.

Option 1:
Select sites that are within ½ mile walking distance to a rail station.
Exemplary Performance: Institute a Comprehensive Transit Management Plan that demonstrates a quantifiable reduction in personal automobile use through any of multiple alternative options. Only one point is available for implementing such a plan under SS Credit 4, Alternative Transportation.
Option 2:
Select sites that are within ¼ mile to two or more bus lines.
Exemplary Performance: Double transit ridership by: • Locating the project within ½ mile of at least two existing commuter rail, light rail, or subway lines; or • Locating the project within ¼ mile of at least four or more public or campus bus lines.
Option 3: (Schools)
Show that 80% of the students attending the school live within ¾ to 1½ miles walking distance, depending on grade.

IMPLEMENTATION

• Select a site with public transportation access.

DOCUMENTATION & CALCULATIONS

● Identify local rail stations or bus routes serving the project building.

● Develop a site vicinity plan, to scale, and label walking paths between the project building's main entrance and rail stations or bus stops.

● For Schools projects pursuing pedestrian access credit, create an attendance boundary map showing a 3/4-mile radius for grades K–8, or a 1 1/2-mile radius for grades 9 and above.

● In addition to the above, Schools projects should dedicate bike and walking paths leading from the school building to the end of the school property in two or more directions.

Option 1 and Option 2:

On a site plan, draw a ¼- and a ½-mile radius from the main entrance. Identify the dedicated pedestrian routes and bus and rail stops within these circles.

Figure 2 from the LEED Reference Guide for Green Building Design and Construction, 2009. Page 45. Sample Area Drawing.

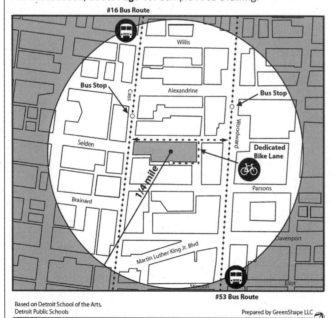

Option 3: (Schools)

Tally the total number of incoming students within the specified walking radius.

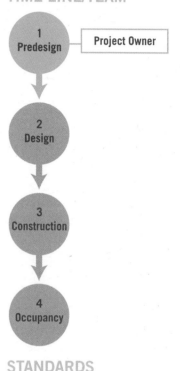

TIME LINE/TEAM

1 Predesign — Project Owner

2 Design

3 Construction

4 Occupancy

STANDARDS

None

NOTES

A school bus system may count as one of the bus lines for Option 2 for Schools projects.

If a rail system is sited, planned, and funded at the time the project is complete, this satisfies the credit.

SS Credit 4.2: Alternative Transportation, Bicycle Storage and Changing Rooms

KEY TERMS

FULL-TIME EQUIVALENT (FTE)

TRANSIENT USERS

RELATED CREDITS

 SS Credit 6: Stormwater Design

 SS Credit 7.1: Heat Island Effect – Nonroof

INTENT

To reduce pollution and land development impacts from automobile use.

REQUIREMENTS

NC:

Case 1: Commercial or Institutional Projects
Provide bike parking for 5% of peak occupants, and showers and changing rooms for 0.5% of full-time equivalent (FTE) occupants within 200 yards of the building entrance.

Case 2: Residential Projects
Provide covered bike parking for 15% of occupants.

CS:

Case 1: Commercial or Institutional Projects (less than 300,000 square feet)
Provide bike parking for 3% or more of average occupants AND provide shower and changing facilities in the building, or within 200 yards of a building entrance, for 0.5% of full-time equivalent (FTE) occupants.

Case 2: Commercial or Institutional Projects (greater than 300,000 square feet)
Provide bike parking for 3% of average occupants for up to 300,000 square feet, then an additional 0.5% for the occupants for spaces over 300,000 square feet AND showers and changing rooms for 0.5% of peak occupants within 200 yards of the building entrance.

Case 3: Residential Projects
Provide covered bike parking for 15% of occupants.

Schools:

Provide bike parking for 5% of peak staff and students above 3rd grade level and shower and changing rooms for 0.5% of the FTE within 200 yards of the building entrance.

Exemplary Performance: Institute a Comprehensive Transit Management Plan that demonstrates a quantifiable reduction in personal automobile use through any of multiple alternative options. Only one point is available for implementing such a plan under SS Credit 4, Alternative Transportation.

IMPLEMENTATION

- Provide bike racks, showers, and changing facilities for occupants.
- Design safe biking paths on-site.
- Design covered, secure bike parking for residential occupants.

DOCUMENTATION & CALCULATIONS

Develop a plan showing the location and quantity of bicycle storage and shower facilities, and determine the distance between the facilities and the building entrance.

Example 1 from the LEED Reference Guide for Green Building Design and Construction, 2009.
Page 56. New Construction: College Classroom Building.
Many college buildings house faculty, staff, and students, complicating the calculation of FTEs. In Table 1, the building occupants are separated into full-time and part-time users to simplify the calculation. The number of persons is multiplied by the number of hours they spend in the building each day and then divided by 8 to calculate the FTE value.

Table 1 from the LEED Reference Guide for Green Building Design and Construction, 2009.
Page 57. Sample Occupancy Calculation for College Building.

FTE Staff Occupant Calculations, Parrish Hall										
Occupants	Persons		Person-Hours per Day		Total Person-Hours per Day		Hours per Day per FTE		FTEs	
Full-time staff										
Administrators	8	x	8	=	64	÷	8	=	8	
Faculty	6	x	8	=	48	÷	8	=	6	
Part-time staff										
Faculty	24	x	2	=	48	÷	8	=	6	
Researchers	20	x	4	=	80	÷	8	=	10	
Total FTE staff									30	
Transient Occupant Calculation										
Occupants								Number at Peak Period		
Students								310		
Visitors								6		
Total								316		
Summary										
Total FTE staff								30		
Transient occupants								316		

In this example, the required number of secure bicycle storage space is 30 x 0.05 + 316 x 0.05 = 17.3, or 18 spaces. The required number of changing and showering facilities is 30 x 0.005= 0.15, or 1.

Example 2 from the LEED Reference Guide for Green Building Design and Construction, 2009.
Page 57. Core & Shell: Commercial Office Building up to 300,000 sf.

Many Core & Shell buildings are midsize, single-use commercial office buildings. These buildings are often programmed for single-shift occupancy. An example of the calculations for this type of building follows.

Building square footage: 125,000 sf
Gross square feet per employee (from Appendix 1 or tenant use as applicable): 250 sf/FTE

$$\text{FTE Occupants} = \frac{125{,}000}{250} = 500$$

$$\text{Secure Bicycle Spaces} = 500 \times 0.03 = 15 \text{ Bicycle Spaces}$$

$$\text{Shower and Changing Facilities} = 500 \times 0.005 = 2.5, \text{ or } 3$$

TIME LINE/TEAM

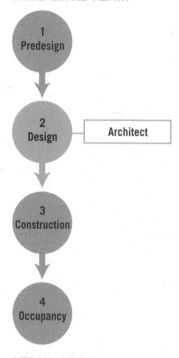

1 Predesign

2 Design — Architect

3 Construction

4 Occupancy

STANDARDS

None

NOTES

Schools must provide dedicated bike lanes that extend to the end of the school property in two or more directions.

Schools calculate bicycle storage based on peak occupancy that includes 5% of all building staff plus 5% of students above third grade.

Showering facilities and changing facilities can be located in another building as long as it is within 200 yards and the project occupants have appropriate access.

Core & Shell projects may use the default occupancy counts found in Appendix 1 of the LEED Reference Guide for Green Building Design and Construction to determine FTE.

SS Credit 4.3: Alternative Transportation, Low-Emitting and Fuel-Efficient Vehicles

KEY TERMS

ALTERNATIVE-FUEL VEHICLES

FUEL-EFFICIENT VEHICLES

FULL-TIME EQUIVALENT (FTE)

GREENHOUSE GASES

HYBRID VEHICLES

LOW-EMITTING VEHICLES

PREFERRED PARKING

RELATED CREDITS

SS Credit 4.4: Alternative Transportation – Parking Capacity

INTENT

To reduce pollution and land development impacts from automobile use.

REQUIREMENTS

Provide preferred parking for low-emitting and fuel-efficient vehicles. Alternatively, provide alternative-fuel fueling stations.

Option 1:
NC/CS Provide preferred parking for 5% of the total parking.
Schools Provide preferred parking for 5% of the total parking, and provide one or more carpool drop-off areas for low-emitting and fuel-efficient vehicles.

Option 2:
NC/CS Provide alternative-fuel fueling stations for 3% of the total vehicle parking.
Schools Provide 20% of buses and maintenance vehicles that use natural gas, propane, or biodiesel or are low-emitting and fuel-efficient.

Option 3:
NC Provide low-emitting and fuel-efficient vehicles for 3% of the FTE occupants, and provide preferred parking for these vehicles.

Option 4:
NC Provide access to a vehicle-sharing program for 3% of FTE occupants.

Exemplary Performance: Institute a Comprehensive Transit Management Plan that demonstrates a quantifiable reduction in personal automobile use through any of multiple alternative options. Only one point is available for implementing such a plan under SS Credit 4, Alternative Transportation.

IMPLEMENTATION

- Designate preferred parking spaces closest to the main entrance for low-emitting, fuel-efficient vehicles with either signage or marking on the pavement.
- Offer discounted parking rates for low-emitting, fuel-efficient vehicles.
- Ensure that low-emitting, fuel-efficient vehicles are defined for users.
- Provide fueling stations for alternative fuels such as natural gas, biodiesel, electricity, or propane.
- Schools: Purchase or retrofit fleet vehicles to use alternative fuels.

DOCUMENTATION & CALCULATIONS

Option 1: (NC/CS/Schools)

On a site plan, highlight the total number of parking spaces and clearly identify preferred spaces for low-emitting and fuel-efficient vehicles. For discounted parking, assemble information about the discount program and how it is communicated to occupants.

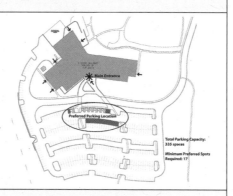

Figure 1 from the LEED Reference Guide for Green Building Design and Construction, 2009. Page 67. Location of Preferred Parking.

Option 2: (NC/CS)

Prepare information about the number of fueling stations provided and the alternative-fuel station types, manufacturers, model numbers, and fueling capacity per station.

Option 3: (NC)

- Provide information on the FTE value and calculation showing the number of qualifying vehicles that must be provided.

Equations 1 from the LEED Reference Guide for Green Building Design and Construction, 2009. Page 65. Total FTE Occupant.

$$\text{Total FTE Occupants} = \frac{\text{Total Occupant Hours}}{8}$$

- Record information about purchased vehicles (make, model, and fuel type).
- Prepare a site plan showing the location of preferred parking spaces.

Option 4: (NC)

- Prepare information about low-emitting and fuel-efficient shared vehicles, including quantity, make, model, and fuel type.

Equations 2 from the LEED Reference Guide for Green Building Design and Construction, 2009. Page 66. Number of Low-Emitting and Fuel-Efficient Vehicles.

$$\text{Number of Low-Emitting and Fuel-Efficient Vehicles} = \frac{\text{FTE Occupancy}}{267}$$

- Retain a copy of the contractual agreement with the vehicle-sharing program.
- Assemble information about the vehicle-sharing program, including estimates of the number of customers served per vehicle and descriptions of its administration.
- Develop a site plan or area map that highlights a pedestrian walkway from the parking area to the project site.

Option 5: (Schools)

- Perform calculations showing the percentage of vehicles or fuel consumption that meets the requirements.
- Assemble information about the alternative-fuel and/or low-emitting or high-efficiency vehicle program.

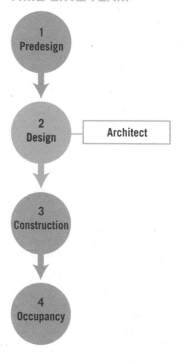

TIME LINE/TEAM

1 Predesign

2 Design — Architect

3 Construction

4 Occupancy

STANDARDS

None

NOTES

Providing a 20% or greater discounted parking rate is an acceptable substitute for preferred parking for low-emitting/fuel-efficient vehicles via Option 1.

There are many vehicles that are not hybrids that meet the definition of low emitting and fuel efficient.

SS Credit 4.4: Alternative Transportation, Parking Capacity

KEY TERMS

PREFERRED PARKING

INTENT

To reduce pollution and land development impacts from automobile use.

RELATED CREDITS

- SS Credit 5.1: Site Development – Protect or Restore Habitat
- SS Credit 5.2: Maximize Open Space
- SS Credit 6: Stormwater Management
- SS Credit 7.1: Heat Island Effect – Nonroof

REQUIREMENTS

"Provide no new parking" is an option in addition to those listed below in every case.

Case 1: Nonresidential Projects

Option 1
Do not exceed local zoning requirements for parking, AND (NC) provide preferred parking for 5% of parking capacity for carpools (same as Schools Option 1).

Option 2
Do not provide parking for more than 3% to 5% of FTE, and provide preferred parking for carpools for 3% to 5% of parking spaces.

Case 2: Residential Projects

Do not exceed local zoning requirements for parking, and support shared-vehicle use.

Case 3: Mixed-Use (Residential With Commercial/Retail) Projects

Split the spaces based on their use. The spaces must meet the requirements associated with residential and commercial FTE for credit calculation.

Schools:

Option 1
Do not exceed local zoning requirements for parking, and provide preferred parking for 5% of parking capacity for carpools.

Option 2
Provide 25% fewer parking spaces than suggested in the Institute of Transportation Engineers' "Parking Generation" study.

Exemplary Performance: Institute a Comprehensive Transit Management Plan that demonstrates a quantifiable reduction in personal automobile use through any of multiple alternative options. Only one point is available for implementing such a plan under SS Credit 4, Alternative Transportation.

IMPLEMENTATION

- Provide preferred parking for carpool vehicles.
- Do not provide any new parking.
- Provide space for carpool drop-off/pickup.

DOCUMENTATION & CALCULATIONS

Prepare information about the amount and type of parking provided, and how carpooling or vanpooling is supported by infrastructure and/or programming. Depending on the option pursued, this might include information about parking capacity, number of preferred parking spaces, number of FTEs, and zoning requirements, or copies of brochures that communicate carpooling and vanpooling support structures to occupants.

NOTES

Buildings that contain less than 10% commercial area must be considered residential.

TIME LINE/TEAM

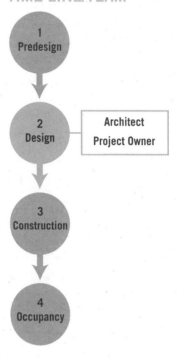

STANDARDS

Institute of Transportation Engineers, "Parking Generation" study, 2003

KEY TERMS

ADAPTED (OR INTRODUCED) PLANTS

BUILDING FOOTPRINT

DEVELOPMENT FOOTPRINT

GREENFIELDS

NATIVE (OR INDIGENOUS) PLANTS

PREVIOUSLY DEVELOPED SITES

RELATED CREDITS

SS Credit 5.2: Site
Development – Maximize
Open Space

SS Credit 6.1: Stormwater
Design – Quantity Control

SS Credit 6.2: Stormwater
Design – Quality Control

SS Credit 7.1: Heat Island
Effect – Nonroof

SS Credit 7.2: Heat Island
Effect – Roof

WE Credit 1: Water Efficient
Landscaping

INTENT

To conserve existing natural areas and restore damaged areas to provide habitat and promote biodiversity.

REQUIREMENTS

Case 1: Greenfield Sites
Limit greenfield site disturbance with setbacks: • 40 feet from perimeter; • 10 feet from hardscape; • 15 feet from roads and utility branches; and • 25 feet from constructed pervious surfaces.
Case 2: Previously Developed Areas or Graded Sites
Restore 50% of the site (minus the building footprint) or 20% of the total site area (including the building footprint), whichever is greater, with native or adapted vegetation.

Exemplary Performance: Restore or protect a minimum of 75% of the site (minus the building footprint) or 30% of the total site (including the building footprint), whichever is greater, with native or adapted vegetation.

IMPLEMENTATION

- Analyze the function of the building to minimize the building footprint. Use native plants in the landscaping design to restore the site to a predevelopment condition.

- Minimize disruption of the site during construction.

DOCUMENTATION & CALCULATIONS

Case 1: Greenfield Sites

Develop site plans that clearly show disturbance boundaries.

Figure 1 from the LEED Reference Guide for Green Building Design and Construction, 2009. Page 81. Example of Disturbance Boundaries.

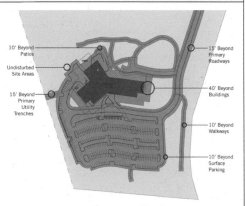

Case 2: Previously Developed Areas or Graded Sites

Prepare site plans that highlight protected or restored site areas, and list native and adapted plant species. Include the square footage of these areas on the site plan.

Figure 2 from the LEED Reference Guide for Green Building Design and Construction, 2009. Page 81. Example of Site Drawing Showing Natural Areas.

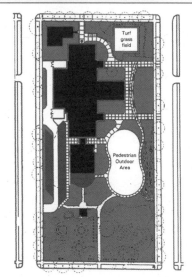

 Building footprint (non-vegetated roof), to be excluded from calculations

Non-vegetated, pedestrian oriented hardscape & non-native vegetation areas, to be excluded from calculations

 Site areas restored with native and adapted vegetative plants

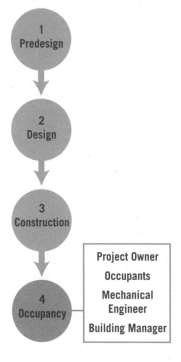

TIME LINE/TEAM

1 Predesign

2 Design

3 Construction

4 Occupancy

Project Owner
Occupants
Mechanical Engineer
Building Manager

STANDARDS

None

NOTES

If also seeking SS Credit 2, Development Density and Community Connectivity, vegetative roofs can contribute to the calculation.

Monoculture plantings (for example, turf) cannot contribute toward the calculation, even if they meet the definition of native or adapted vegetation.

KEY TERMS

BUILDING FOOTPRINT

DEVELOPMENT FOOTPRINT

GREENFIELDS

HARDSCAPE

OPEN SPACE

RELATED CREDITS

SS Credit 6.1: Stormwater
Design – Quantity Control

SS Credit 6.2: Stormwater
Design – Quality Control

SS Credit 7.1: Heat Island
Effect – Nonroof

SS Credit 7.2: Heat Island
Effect – Roof

INTENT

To promote biodiversity by providing a high ratio of open space to development footprint.

REQUIREMENTS

| **Case 1: Sites With Local Zoning Open Space Requirements** |
| Increase site open space by 25% of local code. |
| **Case 2: Sites With No Local Zoning Requirements** |
| Open space should equal the building footprint if there is no zoning. |
| **Case 3: Sites With Zoning Ordinances but No Open Space Requirements** |
| Open space should equal 20% of the site if no open space requirements exist. |

Exemplary Performance: Double the amount of open space required for credit achievement.

IMPLEMENTATION

- Reduce the development footprint by designing a compact parking, road, and building footprint.

- Design vegetated space adjacent to the building.

- Install a vegetated roof.

Exemplary Performance

DOCUMENTATION & CALCULATIONS

Prepare a site plan that highlights qualifying open space. Include calculations that indicate how the required percentage of open space was derived.

NOTES

SS Credit 2, Development Density and Community Connectivity, vegetated roof areas and pedestrian-oriented hardscape areas can contribute to open space requirements. At least 25% of the hardscape area must be vegetated to qualify for credit achievement.

Wetlands and natural ponds can count as open space if the side slopes are gradual enough and vegetated.

Allotted open space must remain open for the life of the project.

TIME LINE/TEAM

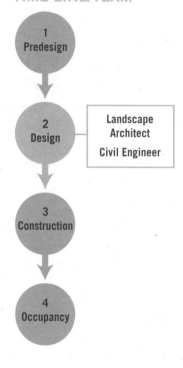

STANDARDS

None

SS Credit 6.1: Stormwater Design, Quantity Control

KEY TERMS

EROSION

IMPERVIOUS SURFACES

STORMWATER RUNOFF

INTENT

To limit disruption of natural hydrology by reducing impervious cover, increasing on-site infiltration, reducing or eliminating pollution from stormwater runoff, and eliminating contaminants.

RELATED CREDITS

SS Credit 5.1: Site Development – Protect or Restore Habitat

SS Credit 5.2: Site Development – Maximize Open Space

SS Credit 6.2: Stormwater Design – Quality Control

REQUIREMENTS

Case 1: Existing Imperviousness = 50% or Less of Total Site Area
Option 1 Postdevelopment discharge (rate and volume) should not exceed the predevelopment discharge rates.
Option 2 Implement a stormwater management plan that protects receiving stream channels from excess erosion.
Case 2: Existing Imperviousness = 50% or More of Total Site Area
Decrease the stormwater runoff (volume only) from the two-year, 24-hour design storm by 25%.

Exemplary Performance: No standardized exemplary performance option has been established, but project teams may apply for exemplary performance by documenting an approach to capture and treat stormwater runoff that is above and beyond the credit requirements. Only one exemplary performance credit may be achieved for SS Credit 6, Stormwater Design.

IMPLEMENTATION

- Reduce the amount of hardscaped area to encourage natural infiltration.

- Mitigate stormwater runoff by designing retention ponds, vegetated filter strips, and vegetated roofs and clustering development.

- Collect or "harvest" stormwater in tanks for reuse in irrigation or toilet flushing.

DOCUMENTATION & CALCULATIONS

● Provide calculations for the rate and volume of pre- and postdevelopment conditions. Calculations may be completed using computer-based software programs or acceptable methodology. To complete the calculations without a software program, you will need the following information:

Equation 1 from the LEED Reference Guide for Green Building Design and Construction, 2009. Page 95. Volume of Captured Runoff.

$$V_r \text{ (cubic feet)} = \frac{(P)(Rv)(A)}{12''}$$

Where Vr = volume of captured runoff
   P = average rainfall event (inches)
   Rv = 0.05 + (0.009)(I) where I = percentage impervious of collection surface
   A = area of collection surface (sf)

Equation 2 from the LEED Reference Guide for Green Building Design and Construction, 2009. Page 95. Minimum Drawdown Rate.

$$Q_r \text{ (cubic feet per second)} = \frac{\text{Tank Capacity (cubic feet)}}{\text{Rainfall Event Interval (seconds)}}$$

Where Qr = minimum drawdown rate

● List stormwater management strategies and record the percentage of rainfall each is designed to handle.

Figure 1 from the LEED Reference Guide for Green Building Design and Construction, 2009. Page 96. Sample Site Plan.

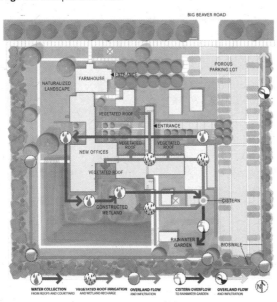

TIME LINE/TEAM

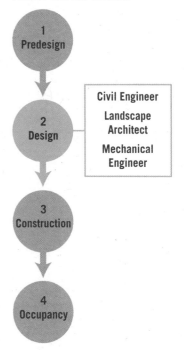

1 Predesign

2 Design — Civil Engineer / Landscape Architect / Mechanical Engineer

3 Construction

4 Occupancy

STANDARDS

None

NOTES

Schools can achieve this point only via SS Prerequisite 2: Environmental Site Assessment and by remediating the site contamination.

SS Credit 6.2: Stormwater Design, Quality Control

KEY TERMS

IMPERVIOUS SURFACES

RETENTION PONDS

STORMWATER RUNOFF

TOTAL SUSPENDED SOLIDS (TSS)

RELATED CREDITS

SS Credit 5.1: Site Development – Protect or Restore Habitat

SS Credit 5.2: Maximize Open Space

SS Credit 7.1: Heat Island Effect – Nonroof

SS Credit 7.2: Heat Island Effect – Roof

INTENT

To rehabilitate damaged sites where development is complicated by environmental contamination and to reduce pressure on undeveloped land.

REQUIREMENTS

Option 1:
Capture and treat 90% of the average annual stormwater runoff AND remove 80% of the total suspended solids.
Option 2:
Provide in-field performance data that conform to acceptable protocols for best management practices monitoring.

Exemplary Performance: No standardized exemplary performance option has been established, but project teams may apply for exemplary performance by documenting an approach to capture and treat stormwater runoff that is above and beyond the credit requirements. Only one exemplary performance credit may be achieved for SS Credit 6, Stormwater Design.

IMPLEMENTATION

- Design vegetated swales or pervious paving to capture and treat runoff.

- Install mechanical filtration devices, vegetated roofs, or rainwater cisterns that allow sediment to settle rather than clog natural waterways.

DOCUMENTATION & CALCULATIONS

- Develop a list of best management practices used to treat stormwater and a description of the contribution of each to stormwater filtration.

- For structural controls, list and describe the pollutant removal performance of each measure; determine the percentage of annual rainfall treated by each.

NOTES

None

TIME LINE/TEAM

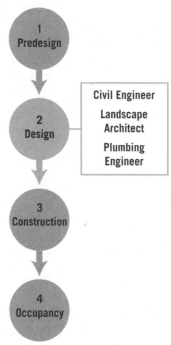

1 Predesign

2 Design — Civil Engineer, Landscape Architect, Plumbing Engineer

3 Construction

4 Occupancy

STANDARDS

None

SS Credit 7.1: Heat Island Effect, Nonroof

KEY TERMS

ALBEDO

EMISSIVITY

HEAT ISLAND EFFECT

IMPERVIOUS SURFACES

INFRARED (OR THERMAL) EMITTANCE

OPEN-GRID PAVEMENT

PERVIOUSNESS

SOLAR REFLECTANCE INDEX (SRI)

RELATED CREDITS

SS Credit 5.2: Site Development – Maximize Open Space

SS Credit 6.1: Stormwater Design – Quantity Control

SS Credit 6.2: Stormwater Design – Quality Control

WE Credit 1: Water Efficient Landscaping

INTENT

To reduce heat islands to minimize their impact on microclimates and human and wildlife habitats.

REQUIREMENTS

Option 1:
For 50% of all hardscape, use a combination of shading, high-reflective hardscape surfaces (29 SRI), and/or open-grid paving.
Option 2:
Place 50% of all parking under cover.

Exemplary Performance: Double the credit requirements for either option (100%).

IMPLEMENTATION

- Select light-colored paving material that reflects rather than absorbs sunlight.
- Plant vegetation that will provide shade for the site's hardscape.
- Limit the amount of hardscape overall by using open-grid pavement systems and putting parking under cover.

NOTES

- The shaded area from landscaping can be the five-year projected area.
- The roof surface for covered parking areas needs to be SRI 29 or better.
- The site and building footprint areas used in Option 1 need to be consistent across the following credits:
  - SS Credit 5.2: Site Development, Maximize Open Space;
  - SS Credit 6.1: Stormwater Design, Quantity Control;
  - SS Credit 6.2: Stormwater Design, Quality Control;
  - WE Credit 1: Water Efficient Landscaping; and
  - MR Credit 1: Building Reuse.
- If Option 2 is pursued, the number of parking spaces needs to be consistent with SS Credit 4.4, Alternative Transportation, Parking Capacity.

DOCUMENTATION & CALCULATIONS

Option 1:

- Prepare a site plan that highlights all nonroof hardscape areas. Clearly label each portion of hardscape that counts toward credit achievement, including the area in square feet. List information about compliant surfaces, including the SRI values of reflective paving materials, shaded areas, and characteristics of any open-grid paving system used.

- For shaded areas, calculate the shade that will be provided after five years of growth at 10 a.m., 12 noon, and 3 p.m. on the summer solstice. The arithmetic mean (average) of these three values will be used as the effective shaded area.

Figure 1 from the LEED Reference Guide for Green Building Design and Construction, 2009. Page 115. Shading and SRI for Credit Compliance.

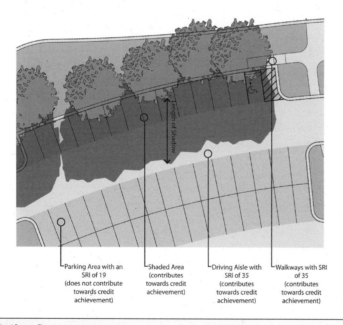

Length of Shadow

Parking Area with an SRI of 19 (does not contribute towards credit achievement)

Shaded Area (contributes towards credit achievement)

Driving Aisle with SRI of 35 (contributes towards credit achievement)

Walkways with SRI of 35 (contributes towards credit achievement)

Option 2:

Calculate the area of parking and divide by the area of covered parking. Provide SRI values for the roofs that cover parking areas.

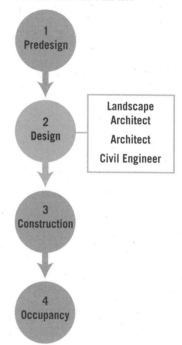

TIME LINE/TEAM

1 Predesign

2 Design

Landscape Architect

Architect

Civil Engineer

3 Construction

4 Occupancy

STANDARDS

ASTM International Standards

SS Credit 7.2: Heat Island Effect, Roof

KEY TERMS

ALBEDO

EMISSIVITY

INFRARED EMITTANCE

SOLAR REFLECTANCE INDEX (SRI)

RELATED CREDITS

SS Credit 5.1: Site Development – Protect or Restore Habitat

SS Credit 5.2: Site Development – Maximize Open Space

SS Credit 6.1: Stormwater Design – Quantity Control

SS Credit 6.2: Stormwater Design – Quality Control

WE Credit 3: Water Use Reduction

EA Credit 1: Optimize Energy Performance

INTENT

To reduce heat islands to minimize their impact on microclimates and human and wildlife habitats.

REQUIREMENTS

Option 1:
Roofing materials must meet the minimum requirements below for at least 75% of the roof surface: • Low sloped: 78 SRI; or • Steep sloped: 29 SRI.

Option 2:
Install a vegetated roof that covers 50% or more of the roof.

Option 3:
Combination of Option 1 and Option 2.

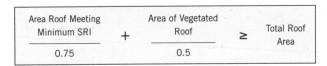

Area Roof Meeting Minimum SRI		Area of Vegetated Roof		
0.75	+	0.5	≥	Total Roof Area

Exemplary Performance: Double the credit requirements for either option (100%).

IMPLEMENTATION

- Select a roof with a high SRI value. A high SRI value generally corresponds to lighter shades of roofing material and greater reflectivity.

- Determine whether a green roof works with the design of the building.

DOCUMENTATION & CALCULATIONS

● Complete calculations showing the percentage of roof area that is compliant. In order to complete the calculations, you will need the following information:

○ Total roof area in square feet, excluding mechanical equipment, solar energy panels, and apertures (skylights, solar tubes, and so on);

○ Roof areas, in square feet, of qualifying reflective and vegetated roofing; and

○ Slope of roof.

Equation 1 from the LEED Reference Guide for Green Building Design and Construction, 2009. Page 124.

$$\left(\frac{\text{Area of Low} - \text{Slope SRI Material}}{78 \times \frac{0.75}{\text{SRI Value}}} + \frac{\text{Area of Steep} - \text{Slope SRI Material}}{29 \times \frac{0.75}{\text{SRI Value}}} + \frac{\text{Vegetated Roof Area}}{0.5} \right) \geq \left(\text{Total Roof Area} - \text{Deducted Area} \right)$$

● Information on roofing products, including their emittance percentages, reflectance percentages, SRI values, and slopes. Retain product specifications that verify product characteristics.

● Prepare roof drawings that show total roof area and the areas of reflective materials or vegetated roof systems.

TIME LINE/TEAM

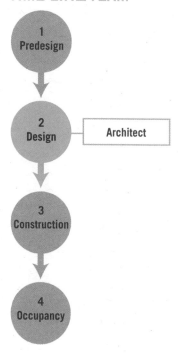

STANDARDS

ASTM International Standards

NOTES

None

KEY TERMS

FOOTCANDLE (FC)

FULL CUTOFF LUMINAIRE

HORIZONTAL FOOTCANDLES

LIGHT POLLUTION

LIGHT TRESPASS

SHIELDING

VERTICAL FOOTCANDLES

RELATED CREDITS

 EA Credit 1: Optimize Energy
Performance

 IEQ Credit 6.1: Controllability
of Systems – Lighting

INTENT

To minimize light trespass from the building and site, reduce sky glow to increase night sky access, improve nighttime visibility through glare reduction, and reduce development impact from lighting on nocturnal environments.

REQUIREMENTS

This credit contains requirements for both interior and exterior lighting systems.

Interior

Option 1:
Reduce interior lighting power by 50% or more between 11:00 p.m. and 5:00 a.m.
Option 2:
Shield all nonemergency luminaires with a controlled device to mitigate light between 11:00 p.m. and 5:00 a.m.

Exterior

Do not exceed lighting power densities set by ANSI/ASHRAE/IESNA Standard 90.1–2007, and classify the project with the appropriate zone as defined in IESNA RP-33 and meet the associated requirements for that zone.

For Schools projects, additional provisions are provided for sports fields.

IMPLEMENTATION

- Design interior lighting so that between the hours of 11:00 p.m. and 5:00 a.m. no light is exiting the building.

- Use full cutoff exterior luminaires to direct light where it is needed.

- Light only areas as required for safety and comfort.

- Create a photometric site plan to model the light levels at and beyond the site boundary, and identify areas that need additional shielding or redesigning to meet the allowable light trespass thresholds.

DOCUMENTATION & CALCULATIONS

- Confirm that the exterior lighting power densities are at or below ASHRAE 90.1–2007 levels.

- Confirm that the percentage of light emitted above horizontal is compliant relative to the environmental zone.

NOTES

The applicable site boundary can be extended in certain circumstances, such as when a private driveway intersects a public roadway.

TIME LINE/TEAM

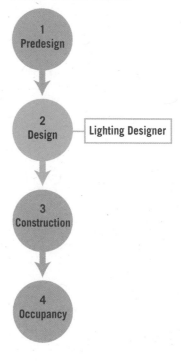

1 Predesign

2 Design — Lighting Designer

3 Construction

4 Occupancy

STANDARDS

ASHRAE 90.1–2007, Section 9; IESNA RP-33

KEY TERMS

None

RELATED CREDITS

WE Credit 3: Water Use Reduction

EA Credit 1: Optimize Energy Performance

EA Credit 3: Enhanced Commissioning

EA Credit 5: Measurement and Verification

IEQ Prerequisite 2: Environmental Tobacco Smoke Control

IEQ Credit 2: Increased Ventilation

IEQ Credit 3: Construction Indoor Air Quality Management Plan

IEQ Credit 5: Indoor Chemical and Pollutant Source Control

IEQ Credit 6: Controllability of Systems

IEQ Credit 7: Thermal Comfort

IEQ Credit 8: Daylighting and Views

INTENT

To educate tenants about implementing sustainable design and construction features in their tenant improvement build-out.

Tenant design and construction guidelines benefit the Core & Shell certified project in two important ways: first, the guidelines will help tenants design and build sustainable interiors and adopt green building practices; second, the guidelines will help in coordinating LEED 2009 for Commercial Interiors and LEED 2009 for Core & Shell Development certifications.

REQUIREMENTS

Create a document for tenants to assist them during design, construction, and occupancy with greening their leasable areas.

IMPLEMENTATION

● Develop guidelines that highlight the green features of the Core & Shell project, stating the project goals.

● Provide information about LEED for Commercial Interiors.

● Outline how future tenants can coordinate design and construction to LEED for Commercial Interiors standards, related to the following measures:

○ Water use reduction;
○ Optimized energy performance—lighting power, lighting controls, and HVAC;
○ Energy use and metering;
○ Measurement and verification;
○ Ventilation and outdoor air delivery;
○ Construction indoor air quality management;
○ Indoor chemical and pollutant source control;
○ Controllability of systems;
○ Thermal comfort;
○ Daylighting and views;
○ Commissioning; and
○ Elimination or control of environmental tobacco smoke.

DOCUMENTATION & CALCULATIONS

- Retain a copy of the tenant design and construction guidelines.

NOTES

Requirements that are included in the lease agreement, such as water-efficient fixtures, may contribute toward credit achievement for the Core & Shell certification.

TIME LINE/TEAM

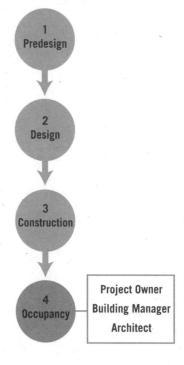

1
Predesign

2
Design

3
Construction

4
Occupancy

Project Owner
Building Manager
Architect

STANDARDS

None

NC: N/A
Schools: 1 Point
CS: N/A

SS Credit 9:
Site Master Plan (Schools)

KEY TERMS

MASTER PLAN

RELATED CREDITS

 SS Credit 1: Site Selection

 SS Credit 5.1: Site Development – Protect or Restore Habitat

 SS Credit 5.2: Site Development – Maximize Open Space

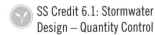 SS Credit 6.1: Stormwater Design – Quantity Control

 SS Credit 6.2: Stormwater Design – Quality Control

 SS Credit 7.1: Heat Island Effect – Nonroof

SS Credit 8: Light Pollution Reduction

INTENT

To ensure that the environmental site issues included in the initial development of the site and project are continued throughout future development caused by changes in programs or demography.

REQUIREMENTS

Earn four of the following seven credits via the LEED project site, and then recalculate them based on the master site or campus:

- SS Credit 1: Site Selection

- SS Credit 5.1: Site Development – Protect or Restore Habitat

- SS Credit 5.2: Site Development – Maximize Open Space

- SS Credit 6.1: Stormwater Design – Quantity Control

- SS Credit 6.2: Stormwater Design – Quality Control

- SS Credit 7.1: Heat Island Effect – Nonroof

- SS Credit 8: Light Pollution Reduction

Develop a site master plan, including existing infrastructure, current construction, and future construction.

IMPLEMENTATION

Develop a site master plan that considers future community needs as well as campus needs.

DOCUMENTATION & CALCULATIONS

- Describe the process of creating the site's master plan.

- Retain a copy of the site's master plan and written verification of its approval.

- For documentation, refer to the qualifying calculations of the eligible credits. Associated credits for SS Credit 9, Site Master Plan, must be recalculated to include all future build-outs indicated in the master plan.

NOTES

None

TIME LINE/TEAM

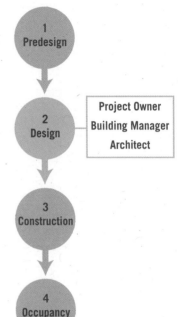

STANDARDS

None

KEY TERMS

None

RELATED CREDITS

SS Credit 2: Development Density and Community Connectivity

INTENT

To make the school a more integrated part of the community by enabling the building and its playing fields to be used for nonschool events and functions.

REQUIREMENTS

Option 1:
Ensure that at least three of the following spaces are available for shared use by the general public: • Auditorium;   • Gymnasium;   • Cafeteria;   • One or more classrooms;   • Playing fields; and   • Parking.
Option 2:
Contract with other organizations to provide at least two dedicated-use spaces, such as a health clinic or police office.
Option 3:
Ensure that at least two of the following spaces, owned by other organizations, are available to students: • Auditorium;   • Gymnasium;   • Cafeteria;   • One or more classrooms;   • Swimming pool; and   • Playing field.

Exemplary Performance: Satisfy two of the three options.

IMPLEMENTATION

Collaborate with community organizations to determine opportunities for joint use.

DOCUMENTATION & CALCULATIONS

List shared spaces on project drawings and retain evidence of communication used to notify the public of shared-space availability or the joint-use agreement.

Figure 1 from the LEED Reference Guide for Green Building Design and Construction, 2009. Page 157. A sample plan demonstrating a joint use of facility.

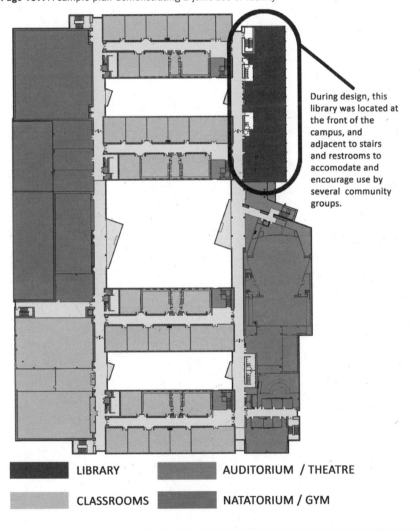

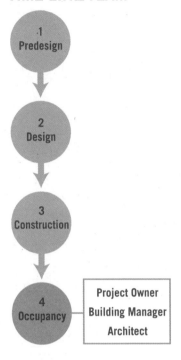

During design, this library was located at the front of the campus, and adjacent to stairs and restrooms to accomodate and encourage use by several community groups.

	LIBRARY		AUDITORIUM / THEATRE
	CLASSROOMS		NATATORIUM / GYM

TIME LINE/TEAM

-1 Predesign

2 Design

3 Construction

4 Occupancy — Project Owner / Building Manager / Architect

STANDARDS

None

NOTES

None

SS CATEGORY REVIEW

1 What site attributes would encourage people to use alternative forms of transportation?

_____

_____

2 What strategies can be employed to help decrease the amount of stormwater leaving a site?

_____

_____

3 What strategies help decrease the heat island effect?

_____

_____

4 What considerations would be important when developing the master plan for a campus?

_____

_____

5 What synergies exist between the Sustainable Sites credits and Water Efficiency credits?

_____

_____

6 Consider building a school in a rural agricultural area. What are the challenges? Which credits might be most important?

_____

_____

SS LEARNING ACTIVITIES

ASK AROUND

Conduct an informational interview with a landscape professional to learn about best practices alternatives to conventional turf for buildings in your area.

THINK ABOUT IT

Consider two sites in your community (perhaps your place of work, gym or favorite restaurant). What sustainable site strategies may be possible to implement and/or already exist? How can each strategy be achieved or why is it not possible?

Strategies	Site A		Site B	
	Yes	No	Yes	No
Rainwater Harvesting				
Reduce Heat Island Effect				
On-Site Stormwater Management				
Minimize Landscape Water Usage				
Increase Access to Mass Transit				

INVESTIGATE

A project owner has assembled a team to design and construct a one-story, 60,000-square-foot office building, to be occupied by his own business. The project team has selected a site at 123 Lane in Big City, California. A portion of the 100,000-square-foot site was formerly occupied by a gas station, and remediation to clean up the contamination has begun.

Which rating system is most appropriate?

Which credits do you currently have enough information for to complete the required documentation and/or calculations?

Are there any recommendations you would be able to make at this point as far as different strategies to consider for site development?

1 A project team is considering multiple sites for a new Core & Shell office tower. Proximity to which of the following will directly affect achievement of one or more credits within the Sustainable Sites category? (Select two.)

a) Proximity to local organic farms

b) Proximity to basic services such as parks

c) Proximity to dedicated bike boulevards

d) Proximity to mass transit such as buses

2 A LEED for New Construction project has a 10,000-square-foot roof and is attempting SS Credit 7.1, Heat Island Effect. The roofing material has a solar reflectance index of 69. Twenty percent of the roof area has a low slope of 1:12, 60% of the roof area has a steep slope of 4:12, and the remaining 20% of the roof area is flat. How much of the flat roof area must be vegetated to qualify for this credit?

a) 0% — the roof already qualifies

b) 25%

c) 50%

d) 75%

e) 100%

f) The project cannot achieve this credit as described above

3 A LEED for Schools project conducted an ASTM Phase I Environmental Site Assessment as required by SS Prerequisite 2, Environmental Site Assessment, which concluded that contamination on the site was likely. It was further determined that the site was never used as a landfill. What must the project do to satisfy the prerequisite requirements?

a) Select a different site

b) Conduct an ASTM Phase II Environmental Site Assessment

c) Perform preventive remediation

d) Contact the EPA regarding a brownfield designation

e) Proceed with design and construction

4 A LEED for New Construction high-rise residential project is attempting to earn SS Credit 4.2, Alternative Transportation, Bicycle Storage and Changing Rooms. The project team anticipates 2,000 residents. How many covered bicycle spaces and how many dedicated commuter showers and changing rooms must be provided for building residents?

a) 100 bicycle spaces, 10 showers

b) 100 bicycle spaces, 0 showers

c) 300 bicycle spaces, 30 showers

d) 300 bicycle spaces, 0 showers

5

A project team is seeking to reduce light trespass onto adjacent properties. Which strategy below specifically addresses light trespass?

a) Install dark sky compliant exterior fixtures

b) Install highly efficient lamps and ballasts

c) Install fixture shielding

d) Increase the mounting height of fixtures

See Answer Key on page 218.

NOTES...

WATER EFFICIENCY

The importance of water to human life, plants, and wildlife can simply not be overestimated. It is critical to all forms of life, and its proper management and discharge must be integral to any sustainable project. The impact of water use goes beyond how much water is consumed, to the energy it takes to get water to a site, and then the treatment of the water after it leaves the site. The Water Efficiency (WE) category encourages the use of strategies and technologies that reduce the negative impacts associated with capturing, storing, delivering, and treating potable water that is consumed in buildings and their landscapes.

WHAT ABOUT WATER EFFICIENCY?

- Is it possible to offset all of a building's water needs by harvesting rainwater?

- What technologies have enabled water savings in the past few decades?

- What emerging technologies hold promise to save even more water in the future?

- What uses require potable water? Are there any uses in typical buildings that may not require potable water?

WATER EFFICIENCY

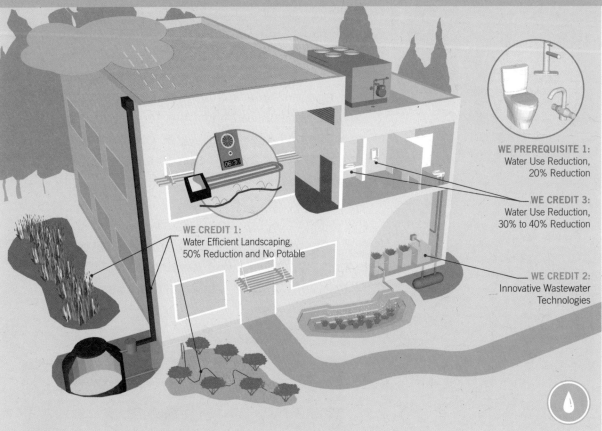

WE PREREQUISITE 1:
Water Use Reduction,
20% Reduction

WE CREDIT 3:
Water Use Reduction,
30% to 40% Reduction

WE CREDIT 1:
Water Efficient Landscaping,
50% Reduction and No Potable

WE CREDIT 2:
Innovative Wastewater
Technologies

THE OVERVIEW

Between increasing demand and shrinking supply, our water resources are strained, threatening both human health and the environment. In short, the current trend in the demand for water is completely unsustainable, with many cities projecting serious water shortages within 10 years. The WE category addresses environmental concerns relating to building water use and disposal and promotes the following measures:

- Reducing indoor potable water consumption;
- Saving energy through water conservation; and
- Practicing water-efficient landscaping.

Buildings' water usage falls into three general categories: indoor water use, outdoor water use for landscaping, and process water. The New Construction and Core & Shell credits focus solely on indoor and outdoor water usage, while Schools also considers process water uses. Process water refers to water used for industrial processes, building systems, and operational processes. Did you know that outdoor water used for landscaping accounts for 30% of the potable water used each day in the United States?

WATER EFFICIENCY

SYNERGIES

Water efficiency is closely tied to the Sustainable Sites category as well as the Energy and Atmosphere category. For example, there are synergies between protecting and restoring habitat and reducing potable water for irrigation. Native plants will require little or no supplemental irrigation and will provide habitat for local flora and fauna. In addition, native and adaptive plants may be used in rain gardens and bioswales that are designed to manage stormwater runoff quantity and quality. From an energy perspective, it is important to note that heating water in buildings can account for 15% of a building's energy usage. Using water efficiently within the building translates into energy savings. Savings are generated when the amount of heated water needed for a particular job can be reduced through smarter design or simple technologies.

CATEGORY HIGHLIGHTS

- This category contains one prerequisite, which is to exceed The Energy Policy Act (EPAct) of 1992 standard by 20%. Up to four additional points are available for exceeding the standard by 40%.

- All WE credits require developing a "baseline" case. The "design" case is compared with the baseline to determine an estimated percentage water reduction.

- The primary standard is the EPAct of 1992 and subsequent rulings in the EPAct of 2005 and the 2006 editions of the Uniform Plumbing Code or International Plumbing Code. ○

WATER EFFICIENCY CREDITS

CREDIT	TITLE	NC	SCHOOLS	CS
WE Prerequisite 1	Water Use Reduction	Required	Required	Required
WE Credit 1	Water Efficient Landscaping	2-4 points	2-4 points	2-4 points
WE Credit 2	Innovative Wastewater Technologies	2 points	2 points	2 points
WE Credit 3	Water Use Reduction	2-4 points	2-4 points	2-4 points
WE Credit 4	Process Water Use Reduction	N/A	1 point	N/A

WATER EFFICIENCY KEY TERMS

KEY TERMS

Adapted (or introduced) plants	Plants that grow reliably well in a given habitat, with minimal winter protection, pest control, fertilization, or irrigation once their root systems are established. Adapted plants are considered low maintenance and not invasive.
Aquifer	An underground water-bearing rock formation or group of formations that supply groundwater, wells, or springs.
Automatic fixture sensors	Motion detectors that automatically turn on and turn off lavatories, sinks, water closets, and urinals. Sensors can be hard wired or battery operated.
Biochemical oxygen demand	A measure of how fast biological organisms use up oxygen in a body of water. It is used in water quality management and assessment, ecology, and environmental science.
Blackwater	Definitions vary, but wastewater from toilets and urinals is always considered blackwater. Wastewater from kitchen sinks (perhaps differentiated by the use of a garbage disposal), showers, or bathtubs is considered blackwater under some state or local codes.
Composting toilet system	See nonwater (or composting) toilet systems.
Conventional irrigation	The most common irrigation system used in the region where the building is located. A conventional irrigation system commonly uses pressure to deliver water and distributes it through sprinkler heads above the ground.
Drip irrigation	A system that delivers water at low pressure through buried mains and submains. From the submains, water is distributed to the soil through a network of perforated tubes or emitters. Drip irrigation is a high-efficiency type of microirrigation.
Evapotranspiration (ET) rate	The amount of water lost from a vegetated surface in units of water depth. It is expressed in millimeters per unit of time.
Graywater	Defined by the Uniform Plumbing Code (UPC) in its Appendix G, "Gray Water Systems for Single-Family Dwellings," as "untreated household waste water which has not come into contact with toilet waste. Graywater includes used water from bathtubs, showers, bathroom wash basins, and clothes washers and laundry tubs. It must not include waste water from kitchen sinks or dishwashers." The International Plumbing Code (IPC) defines graywater in its Appendix C, "Gray Water Recycling Systems," as "waste water discharged from lavatories, bathtubs, showers, clothes washers and laundry sinks." Some states and local authorities allow kitchen sink wastewater to be included in graywater. Other differences with the UPC and IPC definitions can likely be found in state and local codes. Project teams should comply with graywater definitions as established by the authority having jurisdiction in the project area.

Integrated pest management (IPM)	The coordinated use of knowledge about pests, the environment, and pest prevention and control methods to minimize pest infestation and damage by the most economical means while minimizing hazards to people, property, and the environment.
Landscape area	The total site area less the building footprint, paved surfaces, water bodies, and patios.
Metering controls	Controls that limit the flow time of water. They are generally manual-on and automatic-off devices, most commonly installed on lavatory faucets and showers.
Microirrigation	Microirrigation encompasses irrigation systems with small sprinklers and microjets or drippers designed to apply small volumes of water. The sprinklers and microjets are installed within a few centimeters of the ground; drippers are laid on or below grade.
Native (or indigenous) plants	Plants that are adapted to a given area during a defined time period and are not invasive. In North America, the term often refers to plants growing in a region prior to the time of settlement by people of European descent.
Nonpotable water	See potable water.
Nonwater (or composting) toilet systems	Dry plumbing fixtures and fittings that contain and treat human waste via microbiological processes.
On-site wastewater treatment	The transport, storage, treatment, and disposal of wastewater generated on the project site.
Potable water	Water that meets or exceeds the EPA's drinking water quality standards and is approved for human consumption by the state or local authorities having jurisdiction; it may be supplied from wells or municipal water systems.
Process water	Water used for industrial processes and building systems such as cooling towers, boilers, and chillers. It can also refer to water used in operational processes, such as dishwashing, clothes washing, and ice making.
Tertiary treatment	The highest form of wastewater treatment, it includes removal of organics, solids, and nutrients as well as biological or chemical polishing, generally to effluent limits of 10 mg/L biological oxygen demand (BOD) and 5 and 10 mg/L total suspended solids (TSS).
Xeriscaping	A landscaping method that makes routine irrigation unnecessary. It uses drought-adaptable and low-water plants as well as soil amendments such as compost and mulches to reduce evaporation.

KEY TERMS

AQUIFER

AUTOMATIC FIXTURE SENSORS

BLACKWATER

NONPOTABLE WATER

NONWATER (OR COMPOSTING) TOILET SYSTEMS

ON-SITE WASTEWATER TREATMENT

POTABLE WATER

PROCESS WATER

RELATED CREDITS

SS Credit 6.1: Stormwater Design – Quantity Control

SS Credit 6.2: Stormwater Design – Quality Control

WE Credit 1: Water Efficient Landscaping

WE Credit 2: Innovative Wastewater Technologies

WE Credit 3: Water Use Reduction

WE Credit 4: Process Water Use Reduction (Schools Specific)

EA Prerequisite 1: Fundamental Commissioning of Building Energy Systems

EA Credit 3: Enhanced Commissioning

EA Credit 5: Measurement and Verification

INTENT

To increase water efficiency within buildings to reduce the burden on municipal water supply and wastewater systems.

REQUIREMENTS

Reduce building potable water use from the baseline.

Percentage Reduction	Points
20%	Required
30%	2
35%	3
40%	4

Exemplary Performance: Reduce building potable water use by 45%.

IMPLEMENTATION

Install low-flow and low-flush fixtures for toilets, urinals, restroom and kitchen faucets, showerheads, janitor sinks, metering faucets, and commercial prerinse valves.

NOTES

When calculating occupancy, the calculations assume a 1:1 gender ratio unless project conditions warrant an alternative. A narrative description to explain any special circumstances is required.

WE Prerequisite 1: Water Use Reduction, 20% Reduction	Exemplary Performance	

WE Credit 3: Water Use Reduction, 30% to 40% Reduction	Exemplary Performance	

DOCUMENTATION & CALCULATIONS

- Provide a calculator template showing the reduction of water use, listing plumbing fixtures by usage group. In order to complete the calculations, you will need the following information:

  ○ Manufacturer, model number, and flush or flow rate for water closets, urinals, lavatory faucets, showers, kitchen sink faucets, and prerinse spray valves.

  ○ Occupancy information, including the number of building occupants by occupancy type. It is important to understand which FTE occupants use which restrooms if multiple locations with different fixtures are provided.

- The percentage of water use is determined by dividing the design case by the baseline. Use the water use reduction calculator embedded within the LEED Submittal Template.

Retain manufacturers' data showing the water consumption rates, manufacturer, and model of each fixture and fitting.

The LEED Submittal Template is programmed to determine the number of times each type of building occupant uses each fixture type. The default fixture uses by occupancy type are as follows:

Table 2 from the LEED Reference Guide for Green Building Design and Construction, 2009. Page 171. Default Fixture Uses, by Occupancy Type.

Fixture Type	FTE	Student/Visitor	Retail Customer	Resident
	Uses/Day			
Water Closet				
— Female	3	0.5	0.2	5
— Male	1	0.1	0.1	5
Urinal				
— Female	0	0	0	n/a
— Male	2	0.4	0.1	n/a
Lavatory Faucet — duration 15 sec; 12 sec with autocontrol — residential, duration 60 sec	3	0.5	0.2	5
Shower — duration 300 sec — residential, duration 480 sec	0.1	0	0	1
Kitchen Sink, — duration 15 sec — residential, duration 60 sec	1 n/a	0 n/a	0 n/a	n/a 4

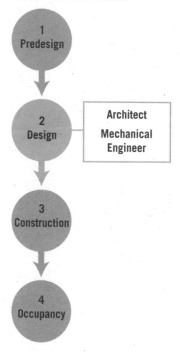

TIME LINE/TEAM

1 Predesign

2 Design — Architect / Mechanical Engineer

3 Construction

4 Occupancy

STANDARDS

The Energy Policy Act (EPAct) of 1992 (and as amended)

The Energy Policy Act (EPAct) of 2005

The 2006 editions of the Uniform Plumbing Code or International Plumbing Code

WE Credit 1: Water Efficient Landscaping, 50% Reduction and No Potable Water Use

KEY TERMS

ADAPTED (OR INTRODUCED) PLANTS

DRIP IRRIGATION

EVAPOTRANSPIRATION (ET) RATE

GRAYWATER

MICROIRRIGATION

NATIVE (OR INDIGENOUS) PLANTS

POTABLE WATER

XERISCAPING

RELATED CREDITS

SS Credit 5.1: Site Development – Protect or Restore Habitat

SS Credit 5.2: Maximize Open Space

SS Credit 6.1: Stormwater Design – Quantity Control

SS Credit 6.2: Stormwater Design – Quality Control

SS Credit 7.1: Heat Island Effect – Nonroof

SS Credit 7.2: Heat Island Effect – Roof

EA Prerequisite 2: Minimum Energy Performance

EA Credit 1: Optimize Energy Performance

INTENT

To limit or eliminate the use of potable water or other natural surface or subsurface water resources available on or near the project site for landscape irrigation.

REQUIREMENTS

Option 1:
Reduce potable water use for irrigation by 50%.
Option 2:
Do not use potable water for irrigation.
Path 1: Use only reused water.
Path 2: Use only landscaping that does not require permanent irrigation systems.

IMPLEMENTATION

- Use native and drought-tolerant plants that can survive on natural rainfall.

- Capture rainwater on-site for irrigation purposes.

- Minimize the amount of turf and use only where needed for recreational or pedestrian use. Turf typically requires irrigation and creates a monoculture that does not encourage biodiversity.

- Specify high-efficiency irrigation systems, such as drip irrigation, which delivers water to plant roots so less water is lost to evaporation.

- Regularly monitor irrigation systems to ensure that they are watering on desired schedules.

- Do not irrigate plants during winter months.

- Mulch landscaped areas to assist with water retention.

DOCUMENTATION & CALCULATIONS

- Provide calculations showing the percentage reduction in water demand, and report what portion of irrigation will come from each nonpotable source (if any). In order to complete the calculations, you will need the following information:

  - Landscape area of project in square feet;
  - Square footage of each major vegetation type—trees, shrubs, ground cover, mixed grass, and turfgrass;
  - Characteristics of each vegetation type, including species factor (ks), density factor (kd), and microclimate factor (kme);
  - Evapotranspiration rate (ETo) for the region; and
  - Data on the irrigation system, including type and controller efficiency (CE).

- Prepare a landscape plan showing a planting schedule and irrigation system.

NOTES

Temporary irrigation can be used for Option 2, Path 2, if it is removed within one year of installation.

TIME LINE/TEAM

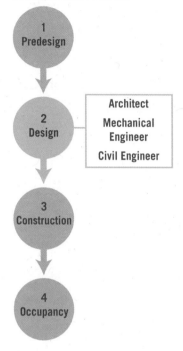

1 Predesign

2 Design

Architect
Mechanical Engineer
Civil Engineer

3 Construction

4 Occupancy

STANDARDS

None

WE Credit 2:
Innovative Wastewater Technologies

KEY TERMS

BLACKWATER

COMPOSTING TOILET SYSTEM

GRAYWATER

NONPOTABLE WATER

ON-SITE WASTEWATER TREATMENT

POTABLE WATER

PROCESS WATER

TERTIARY TREATMENT

RELATED CREDITS

SS Credit 6.1: Stormwater Design – Quantity Control

SS Credit 6.2: Stormwater Design – Quality Control

WE Prerequisite 1: Water Use Reduction

WE Credit 1: Water Efficient Landscaping

WE Credit 3: Water Use Reduction

EA Prerequisite1: Fundamental Commissioning of Building Energy Systems

EA Credit 3: Enhanced Commissioning

EA Credit 5: Measurement and Verification

INTENT

To reduce wastewater generation and potable water demand while increasing the local aquifer recharge.

REQUIREMENTS

Option 1:	Reduce potable toilet water consumption by 50%.
Option 2:	Treat 50% of wastewater on-site.

Exemplary Performance: Treat 100% of wastewater on-site.

IMPLEMENTATION

- Reduce potable water use by using low- or no-flush fixtures, including waterless urinals, composting toilets, or rain/graywater for toilet flushing.

- Install an on-site wastewater treatment system, such as an aerobic reactor or constructed wetlands.

DOCUMENTATION & CALCULATIONS

Option 1:

Using the WE Prerequisite 1 calculations, determine the baseline and design case of only the flush fixtures, to determine whether potable water consumption is reduced by 50%.

Option 2:

- Determine the amount of wastewater compared with the capacity of the wastewater treatment system available.

- Compile information about system schematics and the capacity of any rainwater or graywater systems.

NOTES

Know the baseline assumptions! Baseline fixture types, with their associated daily usage patterns and flow-rate assumptions, are key to understanding where the savings are realized in this credit.

TIME LINE/TEAM

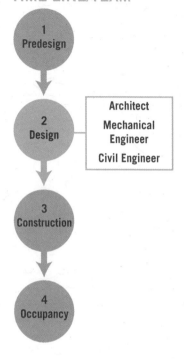

STANDARDS

The Energy Policy Act (EPAct) of 1992 (and as amended)

The Energy Policy Act (EPAct) of 2005

The 2006 editions of the Uniform Plumbing Code or International Plumbing Code

KEY TERMS

PROCESS WATER

RELATED CREDITS

 EA Prerequisite 1:
Fundamental Commissioning
of Building Energy Systems

 EA Credit 5: Measurement
and Verification

INTENT

To maximize water efficiency within buildings to reduce the burden on municipal water supply and wastewater systems.

REQUIREMENTS

Refrigeration equipment must not use once-through cooling with potable water, AND use no garbage disposals, AND use at least four water-efficient process items, such as clothes washers, dishwashers, ice machines, and the like. These systems must be more efficient than the baselines in the credit requirements.

Equipment Type	Maximum Water Use	Other Requirements
Clothes washers[*]	7.5 gallons/ft³/cycle	
Dishwashers with racks	1.0 gallons/rack	
Ice machines[**]	lbs/day>175 20 gallons/100lbs	No water-cooled machines
	lbs/day<175 30 gallons/100/lbs	No water-cooled machines
Food steamers	2 gallons/hour	Boilerless steamers only
Prerinse spray valves	1.4 gallons per minute	
* Commercial CEE Tier 3a—Residential CEE Tier 1 ** CEE Tier 3		

Exemplary Performance: Reduce building process water use by 40%.

IMPLEMENTATION

Assess all water-using process equipment within the school and select water-efficient options.

DOCUMENTATION & CALCULATIONS

- Retain manufacturers' data showing the water consumption rates, manufacturer, and model of each appliance.

- Assemble information about the baseline water use based on industry standards for any equipment that is not listed in the credit requirements.

NOTES

Alternate water-using process items may be used as long as they are 20% more water efficient than industry standards or benchmarks.

TIME LINE/TEAM

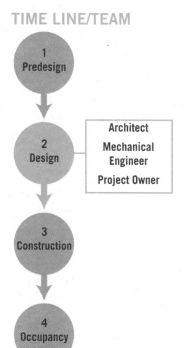

STANDARDS

None

1 What strategies can be employed to reduce the amount of water used for irrigation?

_____

_____

2 How can energy be saved by reducing water usage?

_____

_____

3 How are the Water Efficiency credits and Sustainable Sites credits related?

_____

_____

4 What appliances are covered in the process water use reduction credit that apply to schools only?

_____

_____

5 How do various occupant types affect water savings?

_____

_____

WE LEARNING ACTIVITIES

Complete the water savings calculations for the WE prerequisite and credits for indoor water use reduction based on the information below. Determine what it would take to meet WE Credit 2, Innovative Wastewater Technologies, through water conservation.

- 100 FTE;
- Waterless urinals;
- Dual-flush water closets (0.8/1.6 gpf);
- Low-flow lavatories (0.5 gpm); and
- Conventional shower (2.5 gpm).

INVESTIGATE

Which of the following water efficiency systems do you use or have you seen?

ITEM	USED IT/SEEN IT?
Waterless urinals	
Dual-flush toilets	
Low-flow showerheads and faucets	
Drip irrigation systems	
Rainwater harvesting systems	

If you haven't seen one of the systems, see whether you can find one in your community.

THINK ABOUT IT

Research "typical" landscape practices in your community. See whether you can determine the code requirements for turf, shrubs, and trees. Talk with a landscape architect. Contact your local university extension office and see whether it has information available on evapotranspiration or native turf blends. Visit a xeriscape garden to see whether you can find the person who maintains the garden to ask what lessons he or she has learned in your climate.

WALK AROUND

1 When calculating the water use baseline for WE Prerequisite 1, Water Use Reduction, for a LEED for New Construction project, what flow rate should be used for public lavatories?

    a) 2.5 gallons per minute

    b) 2.2 gallons per minute

    c) 1.0 gallon per minute

    d) 0.5 gallon per minute

2 What are the intended benefits of WE Credit 2, Innovative Wastewater Technologies? (Select three.)

    a) Reduced potable water demand

    b) Improved system redundancy

    c) Increased local aquifer charge

    d) Decreased need for chemical fertilizers

    e) Reduced wastewater generation

    f) Improved stormwater runoff quality

3 Water contaminated with human waste is considered _____.

    a) Brownwater.

    b) Graywater.

    c) Potable water.

    d) Blackwater.

    e) Discharge water.

4 A project is attempting to reduce potable water use by 50% to earn two points under WE Credit 1, Water Efficient Landscaping. Which of the following are viable strategies to achieve this credit? (Select two.)

    a) Reduce the landscaped area.

    b) Increase the irrigation efficiency.

    c) Use nonpotable well water/ groundwater sources.

    d) Design for a low landscape coefficient.

5 A LEED for Schools project is attempting WE Credit 4, Process Water Use Reduction. The project contains a kitchen that serves the entire school district and has specified two dishwashers with racks using less than 1 gallon per rack and one prerinse spray valve using less than 1.4 gallons per minute, as well as one boilerless food steamer using less than 2 gallons per hour. What other systems must be considered to achieve the credit? (Select two.)

    a) Refrigeration equipment

    b) Cooling towers

    c) Ice machines

    d) Garbage disposals

See Answer Key on page 218.

ENERGY AND ATMOSPHERE

The Energy and Atmosphere (EA) category addresses the economic, social, and environmental consequences of energy use. This is done through conserving and generating energy in ways that minimize the negative impacts associated with most current energy systems. These impacts range from the depletion of fossil fuels to contributions to global climate change to the use of additional materials to develop new energy infrastructure as demand increases. EA specifically focuses on energy performance, building systems commissioning, responsible refrigerant use, performance verification, and the use of both on-site and off-site renewable energy.

WHAT ABOUT ENERGY AND ATMOSPHERE?

- Why do we use energy and how do we try to conserve it?

- What makes one source of energy better than another?

- What should be considered when selecting HVAC&R equipment?

- Can a naturally ventilated building with passive cooling be comfortable all year?

- What ways can energy performance be assured over time?

VS.

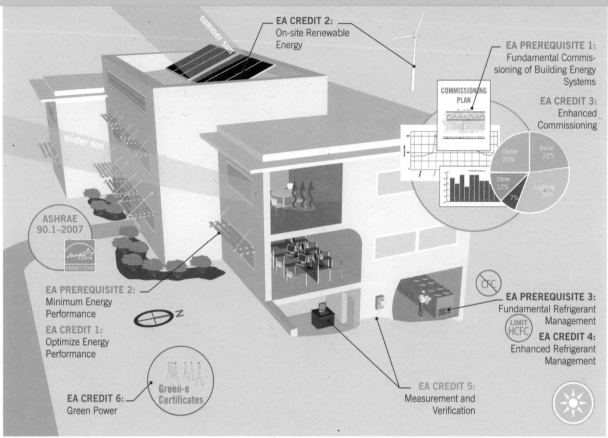

THE OVERVIEW

Green buildings seek to address energy use in multiple ways. First and foremost, they reduce the amount of energy required to operate the building. Additionally, energy use is tracked by monitoring devices and interpreted by building operators to catch deficiencies and identify opportunities for ongoing improvements. To further reduce environmental impacts from power generation, green buildings often utilize renewable energy technologies that generate power on-site, such as solar, wind, biomass, or purchased green power from a utility provider or on the open market.

In addition to energy use and production, the Energy and Atmosphere category addresses refrigerant use. Common refrigerants, which are typically used for air conditioning, are potent greenhouse gases and destroy Earth's stratospheric ozone.

In summary, this category focuses on four components of energy use within buildings and their

ENERGY AND ATMOSPHERE

related atmospheric impacts:

- Conserving energy (energy efficiency);
- Tracking building energy performance—design, commissioning, and monitoring;
- Managing refrigerants to minimize or eliminate atmospheric damage; and
- Using renewable energy.

SYNERGIES

Energy performance within a building is influenced by many aspects of building design and construction. Consider, for instance, that the need for electric lighting is directly related to daylighting strategies and the reflectance of building finishes and furniture. The use of electric lights adds heat to the building, thus creating the need for additional air conditioning in the summer months, when energy demand peaks and is most expensive. Therefore, the reflectance of interior finishes can affect the energy used for lighting, which in turn affects energy use for mechanical cooling equipment.

Water use also has a significant impact on energy use, as the heating and transporting of water for a variety of uses within the building takes energy. Water saving features, such as low-flow lavatories, composting toilets, waterless urinals, and water-efficient dishwashers and ice machines and other such appliances, reduce the energy costs associated with excessive water use.

Maintaining high-quality indoor environmental quality is often seen as a trade-off with maximizing energy performance. While there is a direct correlation to energy use as it relates to using active heating, cooling, and ventilation systems, it is often possible to design a building to reduce or eliminate the energy used to maintain comfort. Natural ventilation strategies, such as providing operable windows or designing the space to take advantage of stack effects, or the use of building mass to store and reject heat can create meaningful energy savings while maintaining superior occupant comfort.

As you can see, energy performance within the building has numerous synergies with building systems, each important in its own right, and contributing to the overall building's energy use.

ENERGY AND ATMOSPHERE

CATEGORY HIGHLIGHTS

- This category represents almost one-third of the total points available to LEED projects, more than any other category.

- A minimum level of energy performance is mandatory for all projects seeking certification under LEED New Construction, Core & Shell, and Schools.

- Commissioning at a fundamental level is required of all LEED projects. Enhanced commissioning goes beyond the mandatory levels and is worth additional points.

- Refrigerants containing chlorofluorocarbons (CFCs) must not be used in the HVAC&R systems. Going beyond simple CFC avoidance, project teams can demonstrate reduced atmospheric impact to earn additional credit.

- Renewable energy use is recognized by LEED. Both on-site and off-site generation are rewarded separately under different credits.

ENERGY AND ATMOSPHERE CREDITS

CREDIT	TITLE	NC	SCHOOLS	CS
EA Prerequisite 1	Fundamental Commissioning of Building Energy Systems	Required	Required	Required
EA Prerequisite 2	Minimum Energy Performance	Required	Required	Required
EA Prerequisite 3	Fundamental Refrigerant Management	Required	Required	Required
EA Credit 1	Optimize Energy Performance	1-19 points	1-19 points	3-21 points
EA Credit 2	On-site Renewable Energy	1-7 points	1-7 points	4 points
EA Credit 3	Enhanced Commissioning	2 points	2 points	2 points
EA Credit 4	Enhanced Refrigerant Management	2 points	1 point	2 points
EA Credit 5	Measurement and Verification	3 points	2 points	NA
EA Credit 5.1	Measurement and Verification—Base Building	N/A	N/A	3 points
EA Credit 5.2	Measurement and Verification—Tenant Submetering	N/A	N/A	3 points
EA Credit 6	Green Power	2 points	2 points	2 points

KEY TERMS

Baseline building performance	The annual energy cost for a building design intended for use as a baseline for rating above standard design, as defined in ANSI/ASHRAE/IESNA Standard 90.1–2007, Informative Appendix G.
Basis of design (BOD)	The basis of design includes design information necessary to accomplish the owner's project requirements, including system descriptions, indoor environmental quality criteria, design assumptions, and references to applicable codes, standards, regulations, and guidelines.
Chlorofluorocarbons (CFCs)	Hydrocarbons that are used as refrigerants and cause depletion of the stratospheric ozone layer.
Commissioning authority (CxA)	The individual designated to organize, lead, and review the completion of commissioning process activities. The CxA facilitates communication between the owner, designer, and contractor to ensure that complex systems are installed and function in accordance with the owner's project requirements.
Energy conservation measures	Installations or modifications of equipment or systems intended to reduce energy use and costs.
Energy simulation model or energy model	A computer-generated representation of the anticipated energy consumption of a building. It permits a comparison of energy performance, given proposed energy efficiency measures, with the baseline.
ENERGY STAR	A rating to measure a building's energy performance compared with that of similar buildings, as determined by the ENERGY STAR Portfolio Manager. A score of 50 represents average building performance.
Enhanced commissioning	A set of best practices that go beyond fundamental commissioning to ensure that building systems perform as intended by the owner. These practices include designating a commissioning authority prior to the construction documents phase, conducting commissioning design reviews, reviewing contractor submittals, developing a systems manual, verifying operator training, and performing a postoccupancy operations review.

Fundamental commissioning	A set of essential best practices used to ensure that building performance requirements have been identified early in the project's development and to verify that the designed systems have been installed in compliance with those requirements. These practices include designating a commissioning authority, documenting the owner's project requirements and basis of design, incorporating commissioning requirements into the construction documents, establishing a commissioning plan, verifying the installation and performance of specified building systems, and completing a summary commissioning report.
Halons	Substances used in fire-suppression systems and fire extinguishers, that deplete the stratospheric ozone layer.
Hydrochlorofluorocarbons (HCFCs)	Refrigerants that cause significantly less depletion of the stratospheric ozone layer than chlorofluorocarbons.
Hydrofluorocarbons (HFCs)	Refrigerants that do not deplete the stratospheric ozone layer but may have high global warming potential. HFCs are not considered environmentally benign.
Leakage rate	The speed at which an appliance loses refrigerant, measured between refrigerant charges or over 12 months, whichever is shorter. The leakage rate is expressed in terms of the percentage of the appliance's full charge that would be lost over a 12-month period if the rate stabilized (EPA Clean Air Act, Title VI, Rule 608).
Lighting power density	The installed lighting power, per unit area.
Owner's project requirements	A written document that details the ideas, concepts, and criteria that are determined by the owner to be important to the success of the project.
Process water	Water that is used for industrial processes and building systems such as cooling towers, boilers, and chillers. It can also refer to water used in operational processes, such as dishwashing, clothes washing, and ice making.
Proposed building performance	The annual energy cost calculated for a proposed design, as defined in ANSI/ASHRAE/IESNA Standard 90.1–2007, Appendix G.

ENERGY AND ATMOSPHERE

Refrigerants	The working fluids of refrigeration cycles that absorb heat from a reservoir at low temperatures and reject heat at higher temperatures.
Renewable energy certificates (RECs)	Tradable commodities representing proof that a unit of electricity was generated from a renewable energy resource. RECs are sold separately from electricity itself and thus allow the purchase of green power by a user of conventionally generated electricity.
Systems performance testing	The process of determining the ability of commissioned systems to perform in accordance with the owner's project requirements, the basis of design, and construction documents.

NC: Required
Schools: Required
CS: Required

EA Prerequisite 1: Fundamental Commissioning of Building Energy Systems

NC: 2 Points
Schools: 2 Points
CS: 2 Points

EA Credit 3: Enhanced Commissioning

KEY TERMS

BASIS OF DESIGN (BOD)

COMMISSIONING AUTHORITY (CXA)

ENHANCED COMMISSIONING

FUNDAMENTAL COMMISSIONING

OWNER'S PROJECT REQUIREMENTS (OPR)

SYSTEMS PERFORMANCE TESTING

INTENT

EA Prerequisite 1:
To verify that the project's energy-related systems are installed and calibrated and perform according to the owner's project requirements, basis of design, and construction documents.

The benefits of commissioning include reduced energy use, lower operating costs, reduced contractor callbacks, better building documentation, improved occupant productivity, and verification that the systems perform in accordance with the owner's project requirements.

EA Credit 3:
To begin the commissioning process early in the design process and execute additional activities after systems performance verification is completed.

REQUIREMENTS

EA Prerequisite 1:
- Select a commissioning authority (CxA).
  - The CxA must have documented experience commissioning at least two previous buildings.
  - For projects over 50,000 gross square feet, the CxA cannot be responsible for project design or construction.
  - The CxA must report directly to the project owner.
- Document the owner's project requirements (OPR) and the design team's basis of design (BOD).
- Include the commissioning requirements in the construction documents.
- Develop and implement a commissioning plan.
- Verify the installation and performance of the following systems:
  - HVAC&R systems (mechanical and passive) and associated controls;
  - Lighting and daylighting controls;
  - Domestic hot-water systems; and
  - Renewable energy systems (such as wind and solar).
- Complete a summary commissioning report.

Exemplary Performance No

EA Credit 3: Enhanced Commissioning

Exemplary Performance Yes

REQUIREMENTS, CONTINUED

EA Credit 3:

- Select an independent third-party CxA. In addition to the requirements of fundamental commissioning, the CxA must:
  - ○ Not be an employee of the design firm; and
  - ○ Not be an employee of, or contracted through, a construction company working on the project.

The CxA must conduct one design review of the OPR, BOD, and design documents prior to the development of the mid-construction documents and back-check his or her comments in the subsequent design submission. The CxA must do the following:

- Review contractor submittals against the OPR and BOD.

- Develop a systems manual.

- Verify building operator training.

- Conduct a review of the building with operations and maintenance staff within 10 months of substantial completion and create a plan for resolving outstanding commissioning-related issues.

NOTES

For projects smaller than 50,000 gross square feet that are not pursuing EA Credit 3, Enhanced Commissioning, the CxA may be a qualified person on the design or construction team who has the required experience.

TIME LINE/TEAM

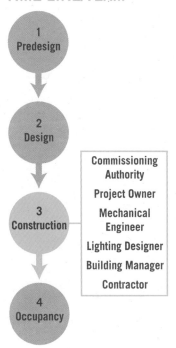

NC: Required
Schools: Required
CS: Required

EA Prerequisite 1: Fundamental Commissioning of Building Energy Systems, Continued

NC: 2 Points
Schools: 2 Points
CS: 2 Points

EA Credit 3: Enhanced Commissioning, Continued

RELATED CREDITS

- SS Credit 8: Light Pollution Reduction
- WE Credit 1: Water Efficient Landscaping
- WE Credit 2: Innovative Wastewater Technologies
- WE Credit 3: Water Use Reduction
- EA Prerequisite 1: Fundamental Commissioning of Building Energy Systems
- EA Prerequisite 2: Minimum Energy Performance
- EA Credit 1: Optimize Energy Performance
- EA Credit 2: On-site Renewable Energy
- EA Credit 5: Measurement and Verification
- IEQ Prerequisite 1: Minimum Indoor Air Quality Performance
- IEQ Credit 2: Increased Ventilation
- IEQ Credit 5: Indoor Chemical and Pollutant Source Control
- IEQ Credit 6: Controllability of Systems
- IEQ Credit 7: Thermal Comfort

IMPLEMENTATION

EA Prerequisite 1: Fundamental Commissioning

- At the beginning of the design phase, select a commissioning authority with the proper experience and independence and complete the owner's project requirements. Instruct the design team to develop its basis of design in accordance with these requirements.

- During design, incorporate the commissioning requirements in the project specification and develop a commissioning plan to govern the commissioning process. Once construction has been substantially completed, the CxA completes functional performance testing to ensure that the systems are operating as intended and meet the OPR.

- After functional testing has been completed, the CxA develops a summary commissioning report.

EA Credit 3: Enhanced Commissioning

- An independent CxA must be selected. An independent CxA is one who is not an employee of a company performing design or construction services for the project.

- During design, the CxA completes a commissioning design review prior to the development of mid-construction documents and back-checks his or her comments to ensure that issues have been addressed. Additionally, the CxA reviews the contractor's submittals as they are submitted to the design team for approval.

- After functional testing, the CxA develops a systems manual. Additionally, the CxA verifies that building operator training has been given to the building's operations and maintenance staff.

- After the building has been operational, the CxA completes a walk-through within 10 months.

DOCUMENTATION & CALCULATIONS

Numerous documents are created to guide, enforce, and facilitate reporting of the commissioning process. The mandatory documents for commissioning are listed below and should be retained by the design team and project owner.

EA Prerequisite 1: Fundamental Commissioning

- Commissioning plan
- Commissioning requirements in construction documents
- Commissioning report
- Functional testing procedures
- Owner's project requirements
- Basis of design

EA Credit 3: Enhanced Commissioning

- Design review
- Submittal reviews
- Systems manual

While engineering calculations are generally necessary to develop functional testing procedures, no specific calculations are required for fundamental or enhanced commissioning.

STANDARDS

None

NC: Required
Schools: Required
CS: Required

EA Prerequisite 2: Minimum Energy Performance

NC: 1-19 Points
Schools:1-29 Points
CS: 3-21 Points

EA Credit 1: Optimize Energy Performance

KEY TERMS

BASELINE BUILDING PERFORMANCE (BASELINE CASE)

PROPOSED BUILDING PERFORMANCE (DESIGN CASE)

ENERGY MODEL

ENERGY STAR

LIGHTING POWER DENSITY

RELATED CREDITS

 SS Credit 7.2: Heat Island Effect – Roof

SS Credit 8: Light Pollution Reduction

WE Credit 3: Water Use Reduction

WE Credit 4: Process Water Use Reduction (Schools only)

 EA Credit 2: On-site Renewable Energy

EA Credit 6: Green Power

IEQ Prerequisite 1: Minimum Indoor Air Quality Performance

IEQ Credit 1: Outdoor Air Delivery Monitoring

IEQ Credit 2: Increased Ventilation

IEQ Credit 6: Controllability of Systems

IEQ Credit 7: Thermal Comfort

IEQ Credit 8: Daylight and Views

INTENT

EA Prerequisite 2: Minimum Energy Performance

To establish the minimum level of energy efficiency for the proposed building and systems to reduce environmental and economic impacts associated with excessive energy use.

EA Credit 1: Optimize Energy Performance

To achieve increasing levels of energy performance beyond the prerequisite standard to reduce environmental and economic impacts associated with excessive energy use.

REQUIREMENTS

Option 1:
Calculate the design and baseline energy use according to Appendix G of ASHRAE 90.1–2007 using a computer simulation to demonstrate a minimum 10% energy savings (5% for major renovations to existing buildings). Points are earned under EA Credit 1, Optimize Energy Performance, for higher energy savings.
Option 2:
Comply with the prescriptive measures of the ASHRAE Advanced Energy Design Guide that are appropriate to the project. This is worth one point under EA Credit 1, Optimize Energy Performance.
Option 3:
Comply with the prescriptive requirements of the New Building Institute's Advanced Buildings™ Core Performance™ Guide. This is worth at least one point under EA Credit 1, Optimize Energy Performance, with up to two additional points available for projects that comply with enhanced performance recommendations.
Schools Only:
Projects must also establish an energy performance rating goal using the EPA's Target Finder Rating Tool.

EA Prerequisite 2: Minimum Energy Performance	Exemplary Performance	No

EA Credit 1: Optimize Energy Performance	Exemplary Performance	Yes

IMPLEMENTATION

Fundamental strategies to reduce energy costs should be considered as follows:

● Reduce energy demand by optimizing building orientation, reducing internal loads, and shifting loads to off-peak periods.

● Harvest free energy using passive strategies such as daylighting, solar heating, and cooling of the thermal mass at night, as well as on-site renewable energy generation from sources such as wind, solar, and geothermal.

● Increase the efficiency of the building envelope, lighting system, and HVAC system.

● Recover waste energy using systems such as energy recovery ventilators and graywater heat recovery.

For Option 1, an energy model must be completed and include all energy costs within and associated with the building.

For Options 2 and 3, follow the prescriptive requirements of the applicable design guide.

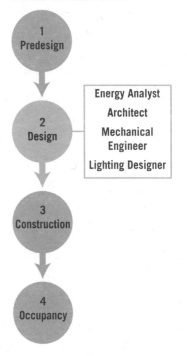

TIME LINE/TEAM

1 Predesign

2 Design

Energy Analyst
Architect
Mechanical Engineer
Lighting Designer

3 Construction

4 Occupancy

DOCUMENTATION & CALCULATIONS

It is important to retain copies of the code compliance documentation prepared by the designers.

For Option 1, numerous subcalculations are input into the energy model, such as lighting power density, fan sizing, and others, although the final computations are completed in the modeling software. Options 2 and 3 have prescriptive requirements and do not require modeling.

NOTES

To use Option 2 or 3, projects must meet minimum qualifying criteria that address occupancy type and project size.

For Option 1, process loads must be the same in the baseline (minimum code compliant) building model as they are in the design model. However, project teams may complete an exceptional calculation to claim credit for measures that reduce process loads.

STANDARDS

ANSI/ASHRAE/IESNA Standard 90.1–2007

ASHRAE Advanced Energy Design Guide for Small Warehouses and Self Storage Buildings 2008

ASHRAE Advanced Energy Design Guide for K–12 School Buildings

New Building Institute, Advanced Buildings™ Core Performance™ Guide

ENERGY STAR Program, Target Finder Rating Tool

ASHRAE Advanced Energy Design Guide for Small Office Buildings 2004

ASHRAE Advanced Energy Design Guide for Retail Buildings 2006

EA Prerequisite 3:
Fundamental Refrigerant Management

KEY TERMS

CHLOROFLUOROCARBONS (CFCS)

REFRIGERANTS

RELATED CREDITS

 EA Credit 4: Enhanced Refrigerant Management

INTENT

To reduce stratospheric ozone depletion.

REQUIREMENTS

Do not use CFC-based refrigerants in new HVAC&R systems. For existing systems, complete a phase-out of all CFC-based refrigerants.

IMPLEMENTATION

The mechanical engineer should specify building mechanical systems that do not contain CFC refrigerants. Alternative refrigerants, such as HCFCs, HFCs, as well as natural refrigerants such as ammonia, carbon dioxide, or simple water, can be used. Depending on the climate and building design, it is often possible to maintain comfort without mechanical cooling.

For major renovation projects where the existing HVAC&R systems contain CFC refrigerant, phase out the use of CFCs through either the retrofitting or replacement of CFC-using systems.

DOCUMENTATION & CALCULATIONS

No calculations.

Assemble cut sheets for building HVAC&R systems, confirming that only non-CFC refrigerants were used.

NOTES

Phase-out plans extending beyond the project completion date will be considered on their merits.

When the replacement or retrofitting of an existing HVAC&R system has a simple payback of more than 10 years, it may be exempted from the credit requirements.

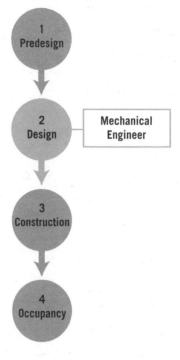

TIME LINE/TEAM

1 Predesign

2 Design — Mechanical Engineer

3 Construction

4 Occupancy

STANDARDS

U.S. EPA Clean Air Act, Title VI, Section 608, Compliance with the Section 608 Recycling Rule

EA Credit 2:
On-site Renewable Energy

KEY TERMS

RENEWABLE ENERGY CERTIFICATES (RECS)

INTENT

To encourage and recognize increasing levels of on-site renewable energy self-supply to reduce environmental and economic impacts associated with fossil fuel energy use.

RELATED CREDITS

EA Prerequisite 1: Fundamental Commissioning

EA Prerequisite 2: Minimum Energy Performance

EA Credit 1: Optimize Energy Performance

EA Credit 5: Measurement and Verification

EA Credit 6: Green Power

REQUIREMENTS

Install on-site renewable energy systems. The level of achievement for New Construction and Schools projects (that is, the number of points) is determined by the percentage of energy costs offset by the renewable energy systems. Under Core & Shell, there is a single threshold.

IMPLEMENTATION

Estimate the energy cost during the design phase to determine how much renewable energy is necessary to meet the project goals, using either a building energy model or the CBECS database. Confirm your estimates once the final energy model is completed.

Eligible renewable energy systems include the following:

- Photovoltaic systems;

- Wind energy systems;

- Solar thermal systems;

- Some biofuel-based electrical systems (those that use eligible biofuels, generally fuel sources that have minimal environmental impact when combusted);

- Geothermal heating systems;

- Geothermal electric systems;

- Low-impact hydroelectric power systems; and

- Wave and tidal power systems.

IMPLEMENTATION, CONTINUED

Ineligible systems include the following:

- Architectural features;

- Passive solar strategies;

- Daylighting strategies; and

- Geo-exchange systems (ground-source heat pumps).

DOCUMENTATION & CALCULATIONS

Determine the value of on-site energy generation and calculate it as a percentage of overall energy cost.

NOTES

If the renewable attributes of the on-site-generated energy are not retained by the project, renewable energy certificates (RECs) equal to 200% of the system's annual rated power output must be purchased from another source. These RECs must be Green-e eligible.

TIME LINE/TEAM

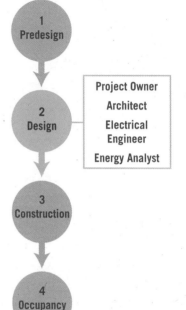

STANDARDS

ANSI/ASHRAE/IESNA Standard 90.1–2007, Energy Standard for Buildings Except Low-Rise Residential

U.S. Department of Energy's Commercial Buildings Energy Consumption Survey (CBECS)

KEY TERMS

CHLOROFLUOROCARBONS (CFCS)

HALONS

HYDROCHLOROFLUOROCARBONS (HCFCS)

HYDROFLUOROCARBONS (HFCS)

LEAKAGE RATE

REFRIGERANTS

RELATED CREDITS

EA Prerequisite 2: Minimum Energy Performance

EA Prerequisite 3: Fundamental Refrigerant Management

EA Credit 1: Optimize Energy Performance

IEQ Credit 7: Thermal Comfort

INTENT

To reduce ozone depletion and support early compliance with the Montreal Protocol while minimizing direct contributions to climate change.

REQUIREMENTS

Do not use fire-suppression systems that contain CFCs, HCFCs, halons, or other ozone-depleting substances.

Use no refrigerants or use refrigerants that minimize or eliminate direct impacts to ozone depletion and climate change.

IMPLEMENTATION

Evaluate the cooling and refrigeration needs of the building to determine whether refrigerant-containing equipment is necessary.

Minimize refrigerant leaks, select equipment with long service lives, and consider low-impact alternatives when selecting refrigerants. All refrigerants have corresponding ozone depletion potential and global warming potential, which is predefined based on the specific type of refrigerant (such as R-410a or R-22). It is critical to balance the ozone depletion potential, global warming potential, and impact on energy performance when selecting appropriate refrigerants for the project.

Select fire-suppression systems that do not contain ozone-depleting chemicals.

EA Credit 4:
Enhanced Refrigerant Management

DOCUMENTATION & CALCULATIONS

The variables necessary to complete the calculation are the refrigerant charge(s), refrigerant type(s), and equipment type(s). With this information for all HVAC&R systems, along with the default values for equipment life, leakage rate, and end-of-life refrigerant loss provided in the LEED Reference Guide for Green Building Design and Construction, the final calculation can be completed to confirm whether the credit requirements have been met. The calculation itself, while detailed in the reference guide, considers the direct global warming and ozone depletion due to the annual and end-of-life leakage of refrigerant.

NOTES

Small HVAC units (containing less than 0.5 pounds of refrigerant) and equipment such as standard refrigerators and small water coolers are not considered by this credit and are excluded from the calculation.

The calculations must assume the default annual and end-of-life leakage rates unless alternate values are preapproved by USGBC. If alternate values are not yet preapproved, the project team may provide documentation from the equipment manufacturer to substantiate its claim. Alternate values not preapproved by USGBC will be evaluated on their merits.

TIME LINE/TEAM

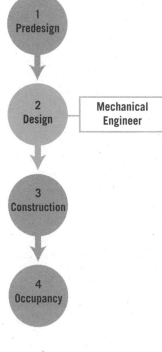

STANDARDS

None

KEY TERMS

ENERGY CONSERVATION MEASURES

RELATED CREDITS

EA Prerequisite 1: Fundamental Commissioning

EA Prerequisite 2: Minimum Energy Performance

EA Credit 1: Optimize Energy Performance

EA Credit 2: On-site Renewable Energy

EA Credit 3: Enhanced Commissioning

INTENT

To provide for the ongoing accountability of building energy consumption over time.

REQUIREMENTS

Option 1:
Create and implement for at least one year a measurement and verification plan following International Performance Measurement & Verification Protocol (IPMVP), Volume III—Option D: Calibrated Simulation. Have in place a plan for corrective action if anticipated energy savings are not realized.
Option 2:
Create and implement for at least one year a measure and verification plan following IPMVP, Volume III—Option B: Energy Conservation Measure Isolation. Have in place a plan for corrective action if anticipated energy savings are not realized.

IMPLEMENTATION

- Create an M&V plan following Option B or Option D of the IPMVP.

- Install submetering equipment on major energy consumers such as HVAC, lighting, and plug loads.

- Collect energy use once the building is occupied.

- Calibrate the energy model with actual energy-use data (Option D).

DOCUMENTATION & CALCULATIONS

Develop an IPMVP-compliant measurement and verification plan.

Diagram the locations of any meters needed for measurement and update as necessary.

NOTES

IPMVP, Volume III—Option B: Energy Conservation Measure Isolation reviews the energy performance of each metered system. It is good for small buildings or single energy conservation measures.

IPMVP, Volume III—Option D: Calibrated Simulation reviews the whole building by adjusting the energy model to align with the actual energy data. It is good for large buildings with interacting energy conservation systems.

TIME LINE/TEAM

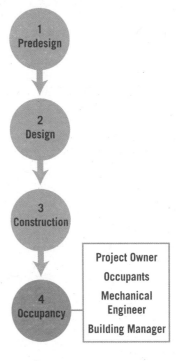

STANDARDS

International Performance Measurement & Verification Protocol, Volume III, EVO 30000.1–2006, Concepts and Options for Determining Energy Savings in New Construction, effective January 2006

EA Credit 5.1: Measurement and Verification, Base Building (CS)

EA Credit 5.2: Measurement and Verification, Tenant Submetering (CS)

KEY TERMS

ENERGY CONSERVATION MEASURES

SUBMETERING

RELATED CREDITS

EA Prerequisite 1: Fundamental Commissioning

EA Prerequisite 2: Minimum Energy Performance

EA Credit 1: Optimize Energy Performance

EA Credit 2: On-site Renewable Energy

EA Credit 3: Enhanced Commissioning

INTENT

To provide for the ongoing accountability of building energy consumption over time.

REQUIREMENTS

EA Credit 5.1:

Option 1:
Create and implement a measurement and verification plan following IPMVP, Volume III— Option D: Calibrated Simulation.
Option 2:
Create and implement a measurement and verification plan following IPMVP, Volume III—Option B: Energy Conservation Measure Isolation.

For both options, the measurement and verification (M&V) plan must include a description of the infrastructure design, identify metering equipment, include one-line electrical drawings, and provide guidelines for tenant submetering.

EA Credit 5.2:

Install an expandable, centrally monitored electronic metering network to accommodate future tenant submetering. Develop a tenant M&V plan to inform occupants of the opportunity and how to use it.

Have in place a plan for corrective action if anticipated energy savings are not realized.

IMPLEMENTATION

- Create an M&V plan following Option B or Option D of the IPMVP.

- Install submetering equipment on major energy consumers such as HVAC, lighting, and plug loads.

IMPLEMENTATION, CONTINUED

● Collect energy use once the building is occupied.

● Calibrate the energy model with actual energy-use data (Option D).

● For EA Credit 5.2, Measurement and Verification, Tenant Submetering, under Core & Shell develop a tenant M&V plan to encourage and enable tenants to make use of the metering system.

DOCUMENTATION & CALCULATIONS

Develop an IPMVP-compliant measurement and verification plan.

Diagram the locations of any meters needed for measurement and update as necessary.

Decide how the tenants will be accountable for their energy use; include specific indications of how the energy use will be determined and how costs will be incurred.

NOTES

IPMVP, Volume III—Option B: Energy Conservation Measure Isolation reviews the energy performance of each metered system. It is good for small buildings or single energy conservation measures.

IPMVP, Volume III—Option D: Calibrated Simulation reviews the whole building by adjusting the energy model to align with the actual energy data. It is good for large buildings with interacting energy conservation systems.

TIME LINE/TEAM

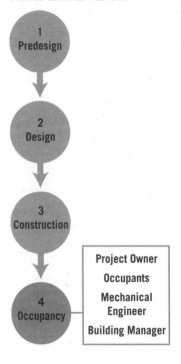

STANDARDS

International Performance Measurement & Verification Protocol, Volume III, EVO 30000.1–2006, Concepts and Options for Determining Energy Savings in New Construction, effective January 2006

EA Credit 6:
Green Power

KEY TERMS

RENEWABLE ENERGY CERTIFICATES (RECS)

RELATED CREDITS

 SS Credit 7.2: Heat Island Effect – Roof

 EA Prerequisite 1: Fundamental Commissioning

 EA Credit 1: Optimize Energy Performance

 EA Credit 3: Enhanced Commissioning

INTENT

To encourage the development and use of grid-source, renewable energy technologies on a net zero pollution basis.

REQUIREMENTS

Purchase 35% of the building's electricity from a Green-e certified source for at least two years.

IMPLEMENTATION

Select a Green-e certified electricity provider or purchase Green-e accredited renewable energy certificates (RECs).

DOCUMENTATION & CALCULATIONS

The estimated energy use can be from either the energy analysis conducted for EA Credit 1, Optimize Energy Performance, or the U.S. Department of Energy's Commercial Buildings Energy Consumption Survey (CBECS).

Develop a contract for green power or REC purchase.

NOTES

Schools projects can purchase the green power at the district or other centralized level and allocate it to project buildings as necessary.

Core & Shell projects use the estimated energy use of the core and shell square footage (excluding current or future tenant areas), with a minimum square footage of 15%.

TIME LINE/TEAM

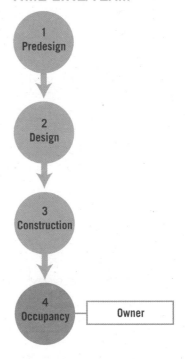

1
Predesign

2
Design

3
Construction

4
Occupancy — Owner

STANDARDS

Center for Resource Solutions, Green-e Product Certification

1   Identify on-site renewable energy systems that are eligible under EA Credit 2, On-site Renewable Energy.

_____

_____

2   What are the elements of commissioning?

_____

_____

3   List some important strategies to reduce energy costs.

_____

_____

4   What factors should be considered when selecting the building HVAC system?

_____

_____

Identify an empty site within your community and imagine that a new, two-story core and shell building is currently being designed for this site. Evaluate options for on-site renewable energy systems given existing site factors and microclimate. Consider solar, wind, geothermal, and others as appropriate. Estimate how much of the building's core and shell energy needs can be generated on-site using your knowledge of available renewable energy technologies. If you are participating as part of a study group, break into groups of three or four for this activity.

THINK ABOUT IT

Imagine you are the project owner for a new, 10-story office building that is in predesign within your community. The project team has not decided whether it will pursue EA Credit 3, Enhanced Commissioning, although it will certainly pursue EA Prerequisite 1, Fundamental Commissioning of Building Energy Systems. Create a request for proposal (RFP) for a commissioning authority for the project. Be sure that the RFP identifies all the required aspects of fundamental commissioning while requesting that the enhanced commissioning elements be provided as an add-on option. Ensure that the RFP identifies the qualifications necessary for the commissioning authority to successfully perform commissioning in accordance with LEED requirements.

PUT IT IN PRACTICE

Identify two buildings in your community, preferably ones about whose operation you have specific knowledge. List some of the buildings' individual elements (lighting, HVAC, orientation, envelope, renewable energy systems, and so on). If any of their specific components are not known, a reasonable guess will suffice. Compare the components of the two buildings. Which of the two buildings have high-performance systems and which do not? Is there an opportunity for improvement in one or both of the buildings?

INVESTIGATE

EA PRACTICE QUESTIONS

1 A project team is evaluating opportunities to downsize the building mechanical system. Which strategies should be considered? (Select two.)

a) Install a high-performance chiller.

b) Decrease lighting power density.

c) Increase the building mass.

d) Negotiate lower energy rates.

2 The Efficiency Valuation Organization (EVO) has established what standard to describe best practice techniques for measurement and verification?

a) International Performance Measurement & Verification Protocol

b) Green-e Product Certification Requirements

c) The Montreal Protocol for Measurement and Verification

d) Standards and Measures for Performance Verification of Building Systems

e) Measurement and Performance Verification Practices

3 Which systems contribute to achievement of both EA Credit 1, Optimize Energy Performance, and EA Credit 2, On-site Renewable Energy? (Select two.)

a) Biofuel systems powered by combustion of municipal solid waste

b) Biofuel systems powered by animal waste

c) Geo-exchange systems

d) Biofuel systems powered by landfill gas

e) Biofuel systems powered by unrestricted wood waste

f) Daylighting

4 A LEED for Schools project is finishing schematic design, and the owner just selected a commissioning authority for the project. The owner contracted with the commissioning authority to complete all of the necessary steps for EA Prerequisite 1, Fundamental Commissioning, and EA Credit 3, Enhanced Commissioning. Once the owner's project requirements have been documented, what is the next step in the commissioning process?

a) Develop the functional testing procedures.

b) Complete the systems manual.

c) Document the basis of design.

d) Review the submittals.

e) Complete the design review.

5 The design team for a LEED for Core & Shell project is creating a measurement and verification plan that will comply with the requirements for EA Credit 5.2, Measurement and Verification, Tenant Submetering. In order to meet the requirements, what should the team include in the tenant measurement and verification plan to address energy use within the tenant space?

a) Requirements to comply with Option B of the International Performance Measurement & Verification Protocol

b) Documentation and advice for future tenants regarding core and shell infrastructure that will support tenant measurement and verification

c) Requirements that tenants will be responsible for their individual energy costs through the lease agreement

d) A methodology for calculating energy performance risk to the tenants for the first year after occupancy

See Answer Key on page 219.

NOTES...

MATERIALS AND RESOURCES

The Materials and Resources (MR) category focuses on reducing negative environmental impacts related to building materials and material waste generated during construction and operations. The MR category encourages selection of building materials that have reduced impacts associated with extraction, manufacturing, and transportation. The MR category also encourages recycling construction and building occupant waste to reduce the amount of waste that is disposed of in landfills and incinerators.

WHAT ABOUT MATERIALS AND RESOURCES?

What are the impacts of materials and resources used in the built environment?

Why should you recycle?

What does environmentally responsible forest management mean?

How much waste is generated from a large-scale renovation project?

Photo by Mr. Jim Gallop/ Gallop Studio

MATERIALS AND RESOURCES

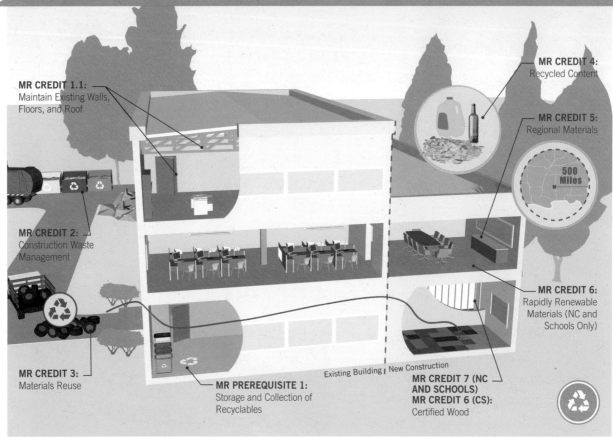

MR CREDIT 1.1:
Maintain Existing Walls,
Floors, and Roof

MR CREDIT 2:
Construction Waste
Management

MR CREDIT 3:
Materials Reuse

MR PREREQUISITE 1:
Storage and Collection of
Recyclables

Existing Building | New Construction

MR CREDIT 4:
Recycled Content

MR CREDIT 5:
Regional Materials

500 Miles

MR CREDIT 6:
Rapidly Renewable
Materials (NC and
Schools Only)

**MR CREDIT 7 (NC
AND SCHOOLS)
MR CREDIT 6 (CS):**
Certified Wood

THE OVERVIEW

Demolition, construction, and subsequent operation of a building generate enormous quantities of solid waste. According to the US Environmental Protection Agency, it is estimated that 136 million tons of construction and demolition debris (versus 209.7 million tons of municipal solid waste) was generated in 1996 - 57% of which was from commercial construction, renovation and demolition activities.[1] The main issues to focus on are the environmental impact of materials used to construct the building and the minimization of landfill and incinerator disposal for materials taken away from the building.

The MR category addresses the following measures:

- Selecting environmentally preferable materials;
- Reducing waste;
- Reducing the number of sources for materials and resources; and
- Reusing and recycling.

1 Department of Natural Resources, Northeast Region. "Building Green at DNR—Northeast Region Headquarters Construction Waste & Recycling."

MATERIALS AND RESOURCES

The Materials and Resources category promotes the selection of materials that have lower environmental impacts than typical building materials. Consideration is given to where a product comes from and what it is made of. Buildings should be designed so that it is easy for occupants and maintenance staff to participate in recycling efforts. During construction, contractors can divert waste materials from landfills and/or incinerators to local recycling centers and significantly reduce the demand on local infrastructure. Recycling construction and demolition debris reduces demand for virgin resources and, in turn, reduces the environmental impacts associated with resource extraction, processing, and, in many cases, transportation.

For school projects, the Materials and Resources category offers opportunities for integrating topics such as resource life cycles, waste reduction, and recycling into the curriculum. In turn, students often become motivated to be involved in conservation efforts at school and in their communities.

Project teams are encouraged to determine the actual total materials cost (excluding labor and equipment) from Construction Specification Institute (CSI) MasterFormat™ Divisions 03–10, plus Section 31.60.00, Foundations and Sections; 32.10.00, Paving; 32.30.00, Site Improvements; and 32.90.00, Plantings. Project teams are also allowed to apply a 45% factor to total construction costs (including labor and equipment) from the same CSI divisions to establish a default total materials cost for the project. Project teams have the option to include materials costs from CSI MasterFormat™ Division 12, Furniture and Furnishings, using either of the above approaches, as long as this is done consistently across all MR credits. Mechanical, electrical, and plumbing components; appliances and equipment; and specialty items such as elevators cannot be included in materials costs. Table 1 contains guidance regarding specification sections included in the cost calculation.

Table 1 from the LEED Reference Guide for Green Building Design and Construction, 2009. Page 337. MR Credit Metrics.

Material	MRc1: Building Reuse	MRc2: Construction Waste Management	MRc3: Materials Reuse	MRc4: Recycled Content	MRc5: Regional Materials	MRc6: Rapidly Renewable Materials	MRc7: Certified Wood
CSI Divisions 3 thru 10	Based on Area	Based on weight or volume. Include demolition and construction waste	Based on replacement value ($)	Based on cost of qualifying materials as a percent of overall materials cost for Divisions 3-10 ($)			Based on cost of FSC wood as a percentage of all new wood ($)
Mechanical							
Electrical							
Plumbing							
Furniture & Furnishings (CSI Division 12)			May be included with Divisions 3-10, if done consistently for credits 3-7				

For either approach (actual or default), the value of total materials cost becomes the denominator for calculating several of the MR credits. The approach selected by the project team must be used consistently across all credits. LEED Core & Shell project teams that use tenant sales or lease agreements to assist with credit compliance must also do so consistently across all MR credits.

Materials calculated toward materials reuse cannot be applied to MR credits for building reuse, construction waste management, recycled content, rapidly renewable materials, or certified wood.

The credits in this category are very closely related, as the materials purchased result in the waste generated for a building. Think of the tenant and building material use as a cycle affected by material selection and sustainable purchasing, waste disposal and waste reduction. Develop purchasing and waste policies in conjunction, implement them at the building, and then track performance. Note that similar standards and calculations are used across the credits.

SYNERGIES

Many of the materials used to construct a building have a direct influence on the energy performance of the building, including different types of wall assemblies, insulation, roofing materials, and glazing. The materials installed in a building also may have an impact on the indoor environmental quality of the space depending on the types of finishes, adhesives, and sealants required.

CATEGORY HIGHLIGHTS

Core & Shell has slightly different credit numbers and corresponding names: MR Credit 1, Building Reuse, Maintain Existing Walls, Floors, and Roof, and MR Credit 6, Certified Wood.

- There are two ways to determine materials cost: actual and default.

- Material cost must be consistent across all MR credits.

- There are many opportunities for exemplary performance that are achievable with careful planning and good specifications.

MATERIALS AND RESOURCES CREDITS

CREDIT	TITLE	NC	SCHOOLS	CS
MR Prerequisite 1	Storage and Collection of Recyclables	Required	Required	Required
MR Credit 1.1	Building Reuse—Maintain Existing Walls, Floors, and Roof	1-3 points	1-2 points	N/A
MR Credit 1	Building Reuse—Maintain Existing Walls, Floors, and Roof	N/A	N/A	1-5 points
MR Credit 1.2	Building Reuse—Maintain Interior Nonstructural Elements	1 point	1 point	NA
MR Credit 2	Construction Waste Management	1-2 points	1-2 points	1-2 points
MR Credit 3	Materials Reuse	1-2 points	1-2 points	1 point
MR Credit 4	Recycled Content	1-2 points	1-2 points	1-2 points
MR Credit 5	Regional Materials	1-2 points	1-2 points	1-2 points
MR Credit 6	Rapidly Renewable Materials	1 point	1 point	N/A
MR Credit 7	Certified Wood	1 point	1 point	N/A
MR Credit 6	Certified Wood	N/A	N/A	1 point

MATERIALS AND RESOURCES

KEY TERMS

Adaptive reuse	The renovation of a space for a purpose different from the original.
Alternative daily cover	Material (other than earthen material) that is placed on the surface of the active face of a municipal solid waste landfill at the end of each operating day to control vectors, fires, odors, blowing litter, and scavenging.
Assembly	An assembly is either a product formulated from multiple materials (for example, concrete) or a product made up of subcomponents (such as a workstation).
Assembly recycled content	The percentage of material in a product that is either postconsumer or preconsumer recycled content. It is determined by dividing the weight of the recycled content by the overall weight of the assembly.
Chain-of-custody (COC)	A tracking procedure for a product from the point of harvest or extraction to its end use, including all successive stages of processing, transformation, manufacturing, and distribution.
Chain-of-custody certification	An award for companies that produce, sell, promote, or trade forest products after audits verify proper accounting of material flows and proper use of the Forest Stewardship Council name and logo. The COC certificate number is listed on invoices for nonlabeled products to document that an entity has followed FSC guidelines for product accounting.
Construction and demolition debris	Waste and recyclables generated from construction and from the renovation, demolition, or deconstruction of preexisting structures. It does not include land-clearing debris, such as soil, vegetation, and rocks.
Construction waste management plan	A plan that at a minimum, identifies the diversion goals, relevant construction debris and materials to be diverted, implementation protocols, and parties responsible for implementing the plan.
Commingled	A mixture of several recyclables in one container.
Embodied energy	The energy used during the entire life cycle of a product, including its manufacture, transportation, and disposal, as well as the inherent energy captured within the product itself.

Existing area	The total area of the building structure, core, and envelope that existed when the project area was selected. Exterior windows and doors are not included.
Fly ash	The solid residue derived from incineration processes. Fly ash can be used as a substitute for Portland cement in concrete.
Forest Stewardship Council (FSC)	An independent, non-governmental, not-for-profit organization established to promote the responsible management of the world's forests. (http://www.fsc.org/about-fsc.html)
Interior nonstructural components reuse	Determined by dividing the area of retained components by the larger of (1) the area of the prior condition or (2) the area of the completed design.
Life-cycle assessment	An analysis of the environmental aspects and potential impacts associated with a product, process, or service.
Rapidly renewable materials	Agricultural products, both fiber and animal, that take 10 years or less to grow or raise and can be harvested in a sustainable fashion.
Refurbished materials	Products that could have been disposed of as solid waste. Once these products have completed their life cycles as consumer items, they are refurbished for reuse without substantial alteration of their forms. Refurbishing includes renovating, repairing, restoring, or generally improving the appearance, performance, quality, functionality, or value of a product.
Regionally extracted materials	Raw materials taken from within a 500-mile radius of the project site.
Regionally manufactured materials	Materials assembled as finished products within a 500-mile radius of the project site. Assembly does not include on-site assembly, erection, or installation of finished components.
Remanufactured materials	Items that are made into other products. One example is concrete that is crushed and used as a subbase.

Postconsumer recycled content	The percentage of material in a product that was consumer waste. The recycled material was generated by household, commercial, industrial, or institutional end users and can no longer be used for its intended purpose. It includes returns of materials from the distribution chain. Examples include construction and demolition debris, materials collected through recycling programs, discarded products (for example, furniture, cabinetry, and decking), and landscaping waste (such as leaves, grass clippings, and tree trimmings). (ISO 14021)
Preconsumer recycled content (formerly known as postindustrial content)	The percentage of material in a product that is recycled from manufacturing waste. Examples include planer shavings, sawdust, bagasse, walnut shells, culls, trimmed materials, overissue publications, and obsolete inventories. Excluded are rework, regrind, or scrap materials capable of being reclaimed within the same process that generated them. (ISO 14021)
Prior condition	The state of the project space at the time it was selected.
Prior condition area	The total area of finished ceilings, floors, and full-height walls that existed when the project area was selected. It does not include exterior windows and doors.
Retained components	Portions of the finished ceilings, finished floors, full-height walls and demountable partitions, interior doors, and built-in case goods that existed in the prior condition area and remain in the completed design.
Reused area	The total area of the building structure, core, and envelope that existed in the prior condition and remains in the completed design.
Soft costs	Expense items that are not considered direct construction costs. Examples include architectural, engineering, financing, and legal fees.
Source reduction	Source reduction reduces the amount of unnecessary material brought into a building. Examples include purchasing products with less packaging.
Sustainable forestry	The practice of managing forest resources to meet the long-term forest product needs of humans while maintaining the biodiversity of forested landscapes. The primary goal is to restore, enhance, and sustain a full range of forest values, including economic, social, and ecological considerations.

MATERIALS AND RESOURCES

Tipping fees	Fees charged by a landfill for disposal of waste, typically quoted per ton.
Waste stream	The overall flow of waste from the building to a landfill, incinerator, or other disposal site.

MR Prerequisite 1:
Storage and Collection of Recyclables

KEY TERMS

SOURCE REDUCTION

TIPPING FEES

WASTE STREAM

RELATED CREDITS

None

INTENT

To facilitate the reduction of waste generated by building occupants that is hauled to and disposed of in landfills.

REQUIREMENTS

NC, Schools, and CS:

Allocate an area for the collection and storage of materials for recycling for the entire building. At a minimum, materials that are required to be recycled are paper, corrugated cardboard, glass, plastics, and metals.

IMPLEMENTATION

- Some recycling activities may affect a building's indoor environmental quality by creating odors, noise, and air contaminants.

- You can't recycle paper, corrugated cardboard, glass, plastics, or metals now? Hopefully, you will be able to soon! Buildings should allocate space for collection and storage in anticipation of future recycling infrastructure.

- Create well-marked and easy-to-find central collection and storage areas for the recyclables.

- A building can consolidate recyclables in a central collection area, as long as they meet the recycling needs of the occupants AND the intent of the credit.

Schools:

- A unique learning opportunity! Create environments for learning and collaboration through student- or occupant-run recycling teams that transport materials from small collection bins to a central collection point.

CS:

- Maintenance and waste management practices for the entire building, including tenant spaces, must be considered.

- Building owners who provide cleaning services for all tenants can control both the space needs and the procedures for removing, storing, and hauling recyclables.

IMPLEMENTATION, CONTINUED

- In buildings where tenants contract their own cleaning services, provide adequate space for recyclable storage and include specific instructions for use within the tenant guidelines.

DOCUMENTATION & CALCULATIONS

- Provide site and floor plans that highlight all recycling storage spaces.

- Keep a record of the recycling plan's size and accessibility to occupants and facility staff; consider whether the planned approach will be adequate.

- Calculations are not required for this prerequisite; however, guidance on the sizing of recycling areas is provided through recommended minimum areas based on the project's square footage.

Table 1 from the LEED Reference Guide for Green Building Design and Construction, 2009. Page 341. Recycling Area Guidelines.

Commercial Building (sf)	Minimum Recycling Area (sf)
0 to 5,000	82
5,001 to 15,000	125
15,001 to 50,000	175
50,001 to 100,000	225
100,001 to 200,000	275
200,001 or greater	500

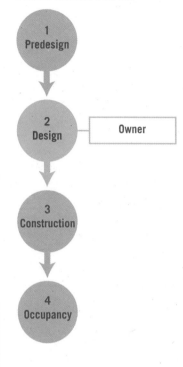

TIME LINE/TEAM

1 Predesign

2 Design — Owner

3 Construction

4 Occupancy

STANDARDS

None

NOTES

- For projects with large site areas, it may be possible to create a central collection area that is outside the building footprint or project site boundary.

- For projects with landscaping, consider designating an area for collecting plant debris.

MR Credit 1.1: Building Reuse, Maintain Existing Walls, Floors, and Roof (NC and Schools)

KEY TERMS

ADAPTIVE REUSE

EXISTING AREA

PRIOR CONDITION

PRIOR CONDITION AREA

REUSED AREA

RELATED CREDITS

 MR Credit 2: Construction Waste Management

 MR Credit 3: Materials Reuse

INTENT

To extend the life cycle of existing building stock, conserve resources, retain cultural resources, reduce waste and reduce environmental impacts of new buildings as they relate to materials manufacturing and transport.

REQUIREMENTS

Maintain the existing building structure and envelope. This includes structural floor, roof decking, and exterior skin and framing and excludes window assemblies and nonstructural roofing material.

Hazardous materials that are remediated as a part of the project must be excluded from the calculation of the percentage maintained.

The minimum percentage of building reuse for each point threshold is as follows:

New Construction

Building Reuse	Points
55%	1
75%	2
95%	3

Schools

Building Reuse	Points
75%	1
95%	2

Core and Shell

Building Reuse	Points
25%	1
33%	2
42%	3
50%	4
75%	5

This credit cannot be pursued if your project includes an addition that is more than six times (for Core & Shell) or twice (for New Construction and Schools) the square footage of the existing building.

Exemplary Performance: CS: 95%

IMPLEMENTATION

- Develop a floor plan that shows the location of existing structural components, exterior and party walls, and exterior windows and doors.

- Confirm the structural and envelope components that will be designated for reuse. Ensure that they are retained and maintained during construction.

DOCUMENTATION & CALCULATIONS

- Prepare a list of the building's structural and envelope elements; include the total area of new, existing, and reused elements.

- Window assemblies and nonstructural roofing materials are excluded from the calculation.

$$\text{Percentage Reuse (\%)} = \frac{\text{Reuse Area (sf)}}{\text{Existing Area (sf)}} \times 100$$

NOTES

If a project incorporates part of an existing building but does not meet the requirements for MR Credit 1.2, Building Reuse, Maintain Interior Nonstructural Elements, you can apply the reused portion toward the achievement of MR Credit 2, Construction Waste Management.

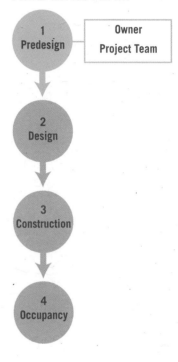

TIME LINE/TEAM

1 Predesign — Owner / Project Team

2 Design

3 Construction

4 Occupancy

STANDARDS

None

MR Credit 1.2: Building Reuse,
Maintain Interior Nonstructural Elements (NC and Schools)

KEY TERMS

ADAPTIVE REUSE

EXISTING AREA

INTERIOR NONSTRUCTURAL
COMPONENTS REUSE

SOFT COSTS

RELATED CREDITS

 MR Credit 2: Construction
Waste Management

 MR Credit 3: Materials Reuse

INTENT

To extend the life cycle of existing building stock, conserve resources, retain cultural resources, reduce waste, and reduce environmental impacts of new buildings as they relate to materials manufacturing and transport.

REQUIREMENTS

NC and Schools

The project must use existing interior nonstructural elements in at least 50% (by area) of the completed building, including additions. Interior nonstructural elements may include interior walls, doors, floor coverings, and ceiling systems.

If there is an addition with more than twice the square footage of the existing building, this credit is not applicable and cannot be achieved.

IMPLEMENTATION

- Initially, it is important to confirm that the items the team would like to reuse can actually be reused. Then, take the necessary steps to retain and maintain them in the finished work.

- Develop a floor plan showing the location of finished ceilings and flooring, interior wall partitions, doors within the interior walls, exterior and party walls, and exterior windows and doors.

DOCUMENTATION & CALCULATIONS

Prepare a list of interior nonstructural elements; include the total area of new, existing, and reused elements.

Equation from the LEED Reference Guide for Green Building Design and Construction, 2009. Page 353. Percentage of Existing Elements.

$$\text{Percentage Existing Elements} = \frac{\text{Area (sf) of All Retained Interior Nonstructural Elements}}{\text{Total Area (sf) of Interior Nonstructural Elements}} \times 100$$

- If a door was used as a door, it must again be used as a door. Fixed items (nonstructural walls and doors) must perform the same function they originally did.

- If a door was used as a door and now it is a floor, it cannot be used for this credit. It is still being reused, however, and can contribute only to MR Credit 3, Materials Reuse.

TIME LINE/TEAM

1 Predesign

2 Design — Architect / Project Owner

3 Construction

4 Occupancy

NOTES

Projects that incorporate part of an existing building but do not meet the requirements for MR Credit 1.2, Building Reuse, Maintain Interior Nonstructural Elements, may apply the reused portion toward the achievement of MR Credit 2, Construction Waste Management.

STANDARDS

None

MR Credit 2:
Construction Waste Management

KEY TERMS

CONSTRUCTION WASTE MANAGEMENT PLAN

COMMINGLED

ALTERNATIVE DAILY COVER

CONSTRUCTION AND DEMOLITION DEBRIS

TIPPING FEES

RELATED CREDITS

 MR Credit 1: Building Reuse

 MR Credit 3: Brownfield Redevelopment

INTENT

To divert construction and demolition debris from disposal in landfills and incineration facilities. Redirect recyclable recovered resources back to the manufacturing process and reusable materials to appropriate sites.

REQUIREMENTS

Recycle and/or salvage nonhazardous construction and demolition debris.

Recycled or Salvaged	Points
50%	1
75%	2

Develop and put into action a construction waste management plan.

Exemplary Performance: 95%

IMPLEMENTATION

- Develop and implement a construction waste management plan. The plan should identify construction haulers and recyclers to handle the materials identified in the plan.

- Ensure that job-site personnel understand and participate in construction debris recycling. Request updates throughout construction to help ensure you're on track.

- Request and hold onto the waste haul receipts, waste management reports, and/or spreadsheets.

- Construction waste may be separated on-site or be commingled and sorted at a facility located off-site.

DOCUMENTATION & CALCULATIONS

Documentation and Calculations:

- Track and keep a log of all construction waste and include the following information:
  - Description of waste;
  - Quantity for each type of waste;
  - Location of disposal or recycling for each type of waste; and
  - Percentage of waste diverted from the landfill as a percentage of total waste.

Example from the LEED Reference Guide for Green Building Design and Construction, 2009. Page 361.

- Existing wood will be treated with care as it is removed from the building so that it can be reused by another local contractor or donated to a reuse store.
- Gypsum board from a previous building remodel will be composted.
- Existing doors will be removed, restored, and stored off-site before being reinstalled during construction.
- The construction waste will be commingled and sorted off-site because the site does not have enough room for sorting materials.
- All cardboard, wood, plastic, and metals will be placed in the same bins.
- The construction waste management plan outlines the responsibility of each subcontractor to recycle lunch waste in a separate, smaller container, to prevent contaminating the construction waste.
- The construction office is instructed to sort paper, plastic, cans, and bottles within the office.
- The contractor takes responsibility for enforcing the plan throughout the construction process.

- Quantities may be calculated by either weight or volume but must be consistent throughout.

$$\text{Percentage of Waste Diverted (\%)} = \frac{\text{Total Quantity of Diverted Waste (weight or volume)}}{\text{Total Quantity of Waste (weight or volume)}} \times 100$$

TIME LINE/TEAM

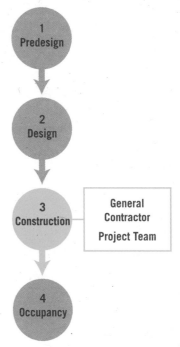

STANDARDS

None

NOTES

Commingled recycling rates for the project must be verified by the facility.

Salvaged materials may include furniture, computers and other electronic equipment, white boards, lockers, doors, lighting, and plumbing fixtures. Salvaged material can be diverted from landfills by donating them to charitable organizations such as Habitat for Humanity, reuse centers, other nonprofit organizations, or other buildings. In addition, materials sold to the community count toward credit achievement.

MR Credit 3:
Materials Reuse

KEY TERMS

REFURBISHED MATERIALS

REMANUFACTURED MATERIALS

RELATED CREDITS

MR Credit 1: Building Reuse

MR Credit 2: Construction Waste Management

MR Credit 4: Recycled Content

MR Credit 5: Regional Materials

MR Credit 6: Rapidly Renewable Materials

INTENT

To reuse building materials and products to reduce demand for virgin materials and reduce waste, thereby lessening impacts associated with the extraction and processing of virgin resources.

REQUIREMENTS

NC and Schools

Use salvaged, refurbished, or reused materials, the sum of which constitutes at least 5% (one point) or 10% (two points), based on cost, of the total value of the building (construction) materials in the project.

Reused Materials	Points
5%	1
10%	2

CS

Use salvaged, refurbished, or reused materials, the sum of which constitutes at least 5%, based on cost, of the total value of materials in the project.

Exemplary Performance: NC and Schools: 15%, CS: 10%

IMPLEMENTATION

- Identify and reuse existing materials found both on- and off-site.

- Use a door for a floor! To qualify as reused, the item must no longer be able to serve its original function and must be installed for a different use or in a different location.

- If the door is still used as the same door, it should be applied to MR Credit 1.2, Building Reuse, Maintain Interior Nonstructural Elements (the same is true for walls, ceilings, and flooring).

- If salvaged furniture is taken from the occupant's previous facility or location, the project needs to demonstrate that these materials were purchased at least two years prior to the project's initiation.

DOCUMENTATION & CALCULATIONS

- Maintain a list of reused and salvaged materials and their corresponding costs. Include construction costs for materials in CSI MasterFormat™, 2004 Edition, Divisions 03–10, 31 (Section 31.60.00, Foundations) and 32 (Sections 32.10.00, Paving; 32.30.00, Site Improvements; and 32.90.00, Plantings).

  OR

- Maintain a list of actual materials costs, excluding labor and equipment.

Equation 1 from the LEED Reference Guide for Green Building Design and Construction, 2009. Page 366. Percentage Reused Materials.

$$\text{Percentage Reused Materials} = \frac{\text{Cost of Reused Material (\$)}}{\text{Total Materials Cost (\$)}} \times 100$$

- Mechanical, electrical, and plumbing components; appliances and equipment; and specialty items such as elevators cannot be included in this calculation. This exclusion is consistent with MR Credits 4, Recycled Content, and 5, Regional Materials.

- Exclude furniture and furnishings (CSI Division 12 components) unless they are included consistently across MR Credits 3–7 (MR Credit 6, Certified Wood, in Core & Shell).

TIME LINE/TEAM

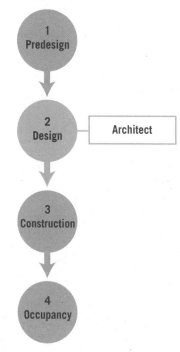

STANDARDS

None

NOTES

Materials that qualify as reused for MR Credit 3, Materials Reuse, cannot be applied to MR Credit 1, Building Reuse; MR Credit 2, Construction Waste Management; MR Credit 4, Recycled Content; MR Credit 6, Rapidly Renewable Materials; or MR Credit 7, Certified Wood.

Off-site salvaged materials can be used for both MR Credit 3, Materials Reuse, and MR Credit 5, Regional Materials.

MR Credit 4:
Recycled Content

KEY TERMS

POSTCONSUMER RECYCLED CONTENT

PRECONSUMER RECYCLED CONTENT

ASSEMBLY RECYCLED CONTENT

FLY ASH

RELATED CREDITS

MR Credit 2: Construction
Waste Management

MR Credit 3: Materials Reuse

MR Credit 5: Regional
Materials

MR Credit 6: Rapidly
Renewable Materials

INTENT

To increase demand for building products that incorporate recycled content materials, thereby reducing impacts resulting from extraction and processing of virgin materials.

REQUIREMENTS

Use materials with recycled content such that the sum of postconsumer recycled content plus half of the preconsumer content constitutes at least 10% (one point) or 20% (two points), based on cost, of the total value of the materials in the project.

IMPLEMENTATION

- Specify products and materials according to CSI MasterFormat™ 2004 classifications for Division 01 recycled-content requirements.

- Research which materials contain high levels of recycled content, or verify which models of a certain product line feature the desired recycled-content values; examples include carpet and ceramic tile.

- Coordinate with subcontractors and suppliers to ensure that materials containing recycled content are available.

NOTES

- Many standard materials contain recycled content because of how they are manufactured.

- Postconsumer recycled content has greater value because of its increased environmental benefit over the life cycle of the product.

- Reusing materials reclaimed from the same process in which they are generated—though good practice—does not contribute toward the recycled content of the material. In other words, putting waste back into the same manufacturing process from which it came is not considered recycling because it was not diverted from the waste stream.

- Reuse of materials includes rework, regrind, or scrap product (Source: ISO 14021); examples are glass culls, which are often reused in the making of new glass.

DOCUMENTATION & CALCULATIONS

- Record product names, manufacturers' names, costs, percentage of postconsumer content, and percentage of preconsumer content.

- Retain cut sheets to document the listed products' recycled content.

Table 1 from the LEED Reference Guide for Green Building Design and Construction, 2009. Page 374. Sample Calculations for Recycled Content.

Total Construction Cost						$600,000

Default Total Materials Cost (45% of Total Construction Cost)						$270,000

Product Name	Vendor	Product Cost	% Postconsumer	% Preconsumer	Recycled Content Value (Equation 1)	Recycled Content Information Source
Structural steel	Multi Steel	$40,000	10.00%	85.00%	$21,000	Structural manufacturer
Underlay aggregate	ABC Foundation	$21,000	20.00%		$4,200	Concrete manufacturer
Particleboard	Sol's Big Boards	$4,000		100.00%	$2,000	Manufacturer
Gypsum board	Gypsum R Us	$8,550		78.00%	$3,335	Manufacturer

Combined Value of Postconsumer + 1/2 Preconsumer Content (Total Recycled Content Value)	$30,535
Combined Value of Postconsumer + 1/2 Preconsumer Content, as a Percentage of Default Total Materials Cost (Total Percent Recycled Content) (Equation 2)	11.31%
Total Points Documented	1

Equation 1 from the LEED Reference Guide for Green Building Design and Construction, 2009. Page 372. Recycled Content Value.

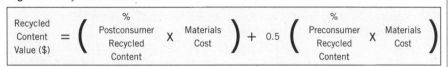

$$\text{Recycled Content Value (\$)} = \left(\frac{\%\ \text{Postconsumer Recycled Content}}{} \times \text{Materials Cost} \right) + 0.5 \left(\frac{\%\ \text{Preconsumer Recycled Content}}{} \times \text{Materials Cost} \right)$$

Equation 2 from the LEED Reference Guide for Green Building Design and Construction, 2009. Page 372. Percentage Recyclec Content.

$$\text{Percentage Recycled Content} = \frac{\text{Total Recycled Content Value (\$)}}{\text{Total Materials Cost}} \times 100$$

- Mechanical, electrical, and plumbing components cannot be included in this calculation.

- Exclude furniture and furnishings (CSI Division 12 components) unless they are included consistently across MR Credits 3–7 (MR Credit 6, Certified Wood, in Core & Shell).

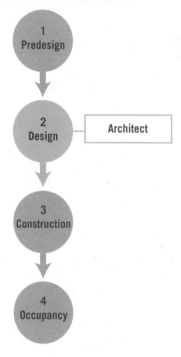

TIME LINE/TEAM

1 Predesign

2 Design — Architect

3 Construction

4 Occupancy

STANDARDS

International Standard ISO 14021–1999, Environmental Labels and Declarations, Self-Declared Environmental Claims (Type II Environmental Labeling)

MR Credit 5:
Regional Materials

KEY TERMS

REGIONALLY EXTRACTED MATERIALS

REGIONALLY MANUFACTURED MATERIALS

INTENT

To increase demand for building materials and products that are extracted and manufactured within the region, thereby supporting the use of indigenous resources and reducing the environmental impacts resulting from transportation.

RELATED CREDITS

MR Credit 3: Materials Reuse

MR Credit 4: Recycled Content

MR Credit 6: Rapidly Renewable Materials

REQUIREMENTS

- Use building materials or products that have been extracted, harvested, or recovered, as well as manufactured, within 500 miles of the project site for a minimum of 10% (one point) or 20% (two points), based on cost, of the total materials value.

- If only a fraction of a product or material is extracted, harvested, or recovered and manufactured locally, only that percentage (by weight) can contribute to the regional value.

IMPLEMENTATION

- If products and construction components are assembled on-site, the individual components that are extracted within 500 miles of the site will be counted toward this credit.

- The contractor should run preliminary calculations based on the construction budget or schedule of values during the preconstruction phase. This will allow the construction team to focus on those materials with the greatest contribution to this credit as early as possible.

DOCUMENTATION & CALCULATIONS

- Create a list of purchased products that were manufactured, extracted, or harvested regionally.

- Record manufacturers' names, product costs, distances between the project and the manufacturer, and distances between the project and the extraction site.

- Retain cut sheets that document where the product was manufactured.

- Where appropriate, maintain a list of materials costs, excluding labor and equipment, for CSI Divisions 03–10, 31 (Section 31.60.00, Foundations) and 32 (Sections 32.10.00, Paving; 32.30.00, Site Improvements; and 32.90.00, Plantings) only; including Division 12 is optional.

Equation 1 from the LEED Reference Guide for Green Building Design and Construction, 2009. Page 381. Percent Local Materials.

$$\text{Percentage Local Materials} = \frac{\text{Total Cost of Local Materials (\$)}}{\text{Total Materials Cost (\$)}} \times 100$$

- Mechanical, electrical, and plumbing components and specialty items such as elevators and equipment must not be included in this calculation.

- Include only materials permanently installed in the project.

- Furniture may be included if it is included consistently in MR Credit 3, Materials Reuse through MR Credit 7, Certified Wood (MR Credit 6, Certified Wood, in Core & Shell).

TIME LINE/TEAM

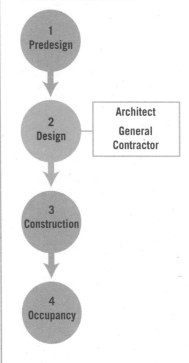

1 Predesign

2 Design — Architect / General Contractor

3 Construction

4 Occupancy

STANDARDS

None

NOTES

- The point of manufacture is considered the place of final assembly of components into the building product that is furnished and installed by the trades workers.

- Using regional building materials reduces transportation activities and associated pollution.

- The support of regional manufacturers and labor forces retains capital in the community.

KEY TERMS

RAPIDLY RENEWABLE MATERIAL

ASSEMBLY

EMBODIED ENERGY

LIFE-CYCLE ASSESSMENT

RELATED CREDITS

 MR Credit 3: Materials Reuse

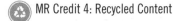 MR Credit 4: Recycled Content

 MR Credit 5: Regional Materials

INTENT

To reduce the use and depletion of finite raw materials and long-cycle renewable materials by replacing them with rapidly renewable materials.

REQUIREMENTS

Use rapidly renewable building materials and products for 2.5% of the total value of all building materials and products used in the project, based on cost.

IMPLEMENTATION

● Identify possible building materials that may be substituted with rapidly renewable products.

● Identify products and vendors in the project specifications and plans, and work with the general contractor to source acceptable alternatives.

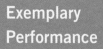

DOCUMENTATION & CALCULATIONS

- Compile a list of rapidly renewable product purchases.

- Record manufacturers' names, materials costs, the percentage of each product that meets rapidly renewable criteria (by weight), and each compliant value.

- Retain cut sheets that document rapidly renewable criteria.

- Where appropriate, maintain a list of actual materials costs, excluding labor and equipment, for CSI Divisions 03–10, 31 (Section 31.60.00, Foundations) and 32 (Sections 32.10.00, Paving; 32.30.00, Site Improvements; and 32.90.00, Plantings) only; including Division 12 is optional.

Equation 1 from the LEED Reference Guide for Green Building Design and Construction, 2009. Page 390. Percent of Rapidly Renewable Materials.

$$\text{Percent of Rapidly Renewable Materials} = \frac{\text{Total Cost of Rapidly Renewable Material (\$)}}{\text{Total Materials Cost (\$)}} \times 100$$

NOTES

Rapidly renewable building materials and products are made from plants that are replenished more quickly than traditional materials, because they are typically planted and harvested within a 10-year or shorter cycle.

Sourcing rapidly renewable materials reduces the use of raw materials, whose extraction and processing have greater environmental impacts.

TIME LINE/TEAM

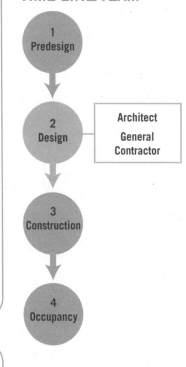

1 Predesign

2 Design — Architect / General Contractor

3 Construction

4 Occupancy

STANDARDS

None

KEY TERMS

FOREST STEWARDSHIP COUNCIL (FSC)

CHAIN-OF-CUSTODY (COC)

CHAIN-OF-CUSTODY CERTIFICATION

SUSTAINABLE FORESTRY

RELATED CREDITS

 IEQ Credit 4.4: Low-Emitting Materials – Composite Wood and Agrifiber Products

 MR Credit 5: Regional Materials

INTENT

To encourage environmentally responsible forest management renewable materials.

REQUIREMENTS

A minimum of 50% of the new wood-based products and materials used in the project, including furniture, must be certified by the Forest Stewardship Council (FSC).

Include only materials permanently installed in the project. Wood products purchased for temporary use (such as formwork, bracing, scaffolding, sidewalk protection, and guardrails) may be included in the calculation at the project team's discretion.

IMPLEMENTATION

- Specify in contract documents that wood products must come from forests that are certified as well managed according to the rules of the FSC. The team should require chain-of-custody documentation.

- Identify FSC-certified wood products suppliers.

- Research and specify quality grades that are most readily available from well-managed forests. Using lower grades of wood (for example, Architectural Woodwork Institute Grades 2 or 3 for lumber or veneer rather than Grade 1) can dramatically reduce pressure on forests, which produce only limited quantities of top-grade timber.

- Collect all vendor invoices for permanently installed wood products, FSC certified or not, purchased by the project contractor and subcontractors.

- Each vendor invoice must conform to the following requirements:
  - All new wood products must be identified on a line item basis;
  - Show cost of each item;
  - Identify FSC-certified products (FSC Pure, FSC Mixed Credit, FSC Mixed [NN]%); and

  - For FSC-Certified Wood Products: Supply a letter from the vendor stating that the products provided are FSC-certified (FSC Pure, FSC Mixed Credit, FSC Mixed [NN]%)

DOCUMENTATION & CALCULATIONS

- Track certified-wood purchases and retain associated chain-of-custody documentation.

- Collect copies of vendor invoices for each certified-wood product.

- Maintain a list that identifies the percentage of certified wood in each purchase.

Equation 1 from the LEED Reference Guide for Green Building Design and Construction, 2009. Page 397. Certified Wood Materials Percentage.

$$\text{Certified Wood Material Percentage} = \frac{\text{FSC-certified Wood Material Value (\$)}}{\text{Total New Wood Material Value (\$)}} \times 100$$

Equation 2 from the LEED Reference Guide for Green Building Design and Construction, 2009. Page 398. Assembly FSC Certified Wood Material Value.

$$\text{Assembly FSC Certified Wood Material Value} = \frac{\text{Weight of FSC-certified Wood in Assembly}}{\text{Weight of Assembly}} \times \text{Assembly Value (\$)}$$

Equation 3 from the LEED Reference Guide for Green Building Design and Construction, 2009. Page 398. Assembly New Wood Material Value.

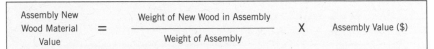

$$\text{Assembly New Wood Material Value} = \frac{\text{Weight of New Wood in Assembly}}{\text{Weight of Assembly}} \times \text{Assembly Value (\$)}$$

Furniture may be included if it is included consistently in MR Credit 3, Materials Reuse, through MR Credit 7, Certified Wood (MR Credit 6, Certified Wood, for Core & Shell projects).

TIME LINE/TEAM

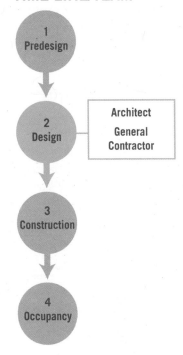

STANDARDS

Forest Stewardship Council's Principles and Criteria

NOTES

Each wood products vendor that invoices FSC-certified products must be chain-of-custody certified by an FSC-accredited certifier.

Exceptions: If it is impractical for a vendor to invoice wood products on a line-item basis because of invoice length, the invoice should indicate the aggregate value of wood products sold by the vendor. For FSC-certified products, the following must be included:

- The vendor's chain-of-custody number;
- A letter from the vendor stating that the products invoiced are FSC certified; and
- A statement on the invoice or letter as to whether the products are FSC Pure, FSC Mixed Credit, or FSC Mixed (NN)%.

1 List the five materials that, at a minimum, are required to have a dedicated area for collection and storage for recycling efforts.

_____

_____

2 What are some referenced standards commonly used throughout the Materials and Resources category that provide testing, certification, and regulatory services? What does each standard do?

_____

_____

3 What building elements are classified as existing building structures?

_____

_____

4 What are classified as existing interior nonstructural elements in MR Credit 1.2, Building Reuse, Maintain Interior Nonstructural Elements?

_____

_____

5 What are the environmental benefits of implementing an effective construction waste management plan?

_____

_____

MR LEARNING ACTIVITIES

Pick five materials and/or products used within your building and research whether they would comply with any of the Materials and Resources credits. Locate designated recycling areas in your building and determine whether they meet LEED requirements. Research local waste hauling companies to determine what construction waste materials can be recycled and how.

INVESTIGATE

Walk through an office or commercial or school building in your community to identify the materials listed below. Which Materials and Resources credit would each item contribute toward?

FEATURE	MR Credit 3.3	MR Credit 4	MR Credit 5	MR Credit 6	MR Credit 7
Workstation (salvaged from previous location)					
Wheatboard Kitchen Cabinetry					
Carpet					
Drywall					
Wooden Conference Table					
Steel Studs					
Ceramic Tiles					
Plywood					
Metal Shelving					
Other					

SITE VISIT

Identify a building product, currently existing or theoretical, that addresses as many of the concerns of the MR category as possible.

THINK ABOUT IT

MR PRACTICE QUESTIONS

1 A project team has specified doors that are made from 40% preconsumer recycled content and that were harvested and manufactured within 500 miles of the LEED project site. The doors are also certified as FSC Mixed 40%. Which LEED credits does this material qualify for? (Choose three.)

   a) MR Credit 3: Materials Reuse

   b) MR Credit 4: Recycled Content

   c) MR Credit 5: Regional Materials

   d) MR Credit 6: Rapidly Renewable Materials

   e) MR Credit 7: Certified Wood

2 Rapidly renewable materials are typically harvested within a _____?

   a) 2-year or shorter cycle.

   b) 5-year or shorter cycle.

   c) 10-year or shorter cycle.

   d) 15-year or shorter cycle.

3 Reusing which of the following building elements contributes toward MR Credit 1.1, Building Reuse, Maintain Existing Walls, Floors, and Roof? (Choose three.)

   a) Structural floor

   b) Window assemblies

   c) Asbestos siding

   d) Wall framing

   e) Building slab

4 The construction of a new building generates 100 tons of waste. Of the new construction waste, 40 tons are recycled, 20 tons are soils that were donated to an adjacent site for infill purposes, 20 tons are incinerated to generate electricity, and the remaining 20 tons are sent to the landfill. What is the overall diversion rate as applicable to MR Credit 2, Construction Waste Management?

   a) 40%

   b) 50%

   c) 60%

   d) 70%

   e) 80%

5 In addition to paper, corrugated cardboard, glass, and plastics, which material must be provided an easily accessible area for collection to comply with MR Prerequisite 1, Storage and Collection of Recyclables?

   a) Food scraps

   b) Yard trimmings

   c) Wood

   d) Metals

   e) Rubber

See Answer Key on page 219.

INDOOR ENVIRONMENTAL QUALITY

The Indoor Environmental Quality (IEQ) category addresses the significant effects that the quality of the interior environment has on occupants. This category seeks to improve ventilation, manage air contaminants, and improve occupant comfort.

WHAT ABOUT INDOOR ENVIRONMENTAL QUALITY?

- What indoor environmental factors affect human health?

- How can occupants achieve thermal comfort in an office with an open floor plan?

- What can occupants teach designers about building performance?

- Can you have too much ventilation?

Photo by Eric Laignel

INDOOR ENVIRONMENTAL QUALITY

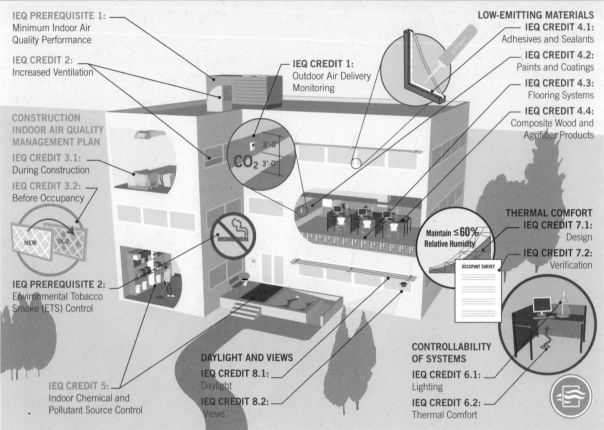

IEQ PREREQUISITE 1:
Minimum Indoor Air
Quality Performance

IEQ CREDIT 2:
Increased Ventilation

**CONSTRUCTION
INDOOR AIR QUALITY
MANAGEMENT PLAN**

IEQ CREDIT 3.1:
During Construction

IEQ CREDIT 3.2:
Before Occupancy

NEW   OLD

IEQ PREREQUISITE 2:
Environmental Tobacco
Smoke (ETS) Control

IEQ CREDIT 5:
Indoor Chemical and
Pollutant Source Control

IEQ CREDIT 1:
Outdoor Air Delivery
Monitoring

CO_2 3'-0" 3'-0"

DAYLIGHT AND VIEWS
IEQ CREDIT 8.1:
Daylight
IEQ CREDIT 8.2:
Views

LOW-EMITTING MATERIALS
IEQ CREDIT 4.1:
Adhesives and Sealants

IEQ CREDIT 4.2:
Paints and Coatings

IEQ CREDIT 4.3:
Flooring Systems

IEQ CREDIT 4.4:
Composite Wood and
Agrifiber Products

THERMAL COMFORT
IEQ CREDIT 7.1:
Design

IEQ CREDIT 7.2:
Verification

Maintain ≤**60%**
Relative Humidity

OCCUPANT SURVEY

**CONTROLLABILITY
OF SYSTEMS**
IEQ CREDIT 6.1:
Lighting

IEQ CREDIT 6.2:
Thermal Comfort

THE OVERVIEW

On average, Americans spend 90% of their time indoors, where pollutant levels may be two to five times higher—and occasionally more than 100 times higher—than outdoor levels. Over the past 20 years, research and experience have improved our understanding of what is involved in attaining high indoor environmental quality and revealed manufacturing and construction practices that can prevent many indoor environmental quality problems.

This credit category addresses environmental concerns relating to indoor environmental quality, occupants' health, comfort, and productivity, ventilation, and air contaminant mitigation. The IEQ prerequisites and credits focus on the following strategies:

- Improving ventilation;
- Managing air contaminants;
- Specifying less-toxic materials;
- Allowing occupants to have control over their environments;
- Providing daylight and views; and
- Reducing background noise and providing good acoustics in schools.

INDOOR ENVIRONMENTAL QUALITY

Since the release in 1987 of EPA reports that designated indoor air pollution as a top environmental risk to public health, assessing and managing indoor pollutants have become the focus of integrated governmental and private efforts. In addition to health and liability concerns, productivity gains are driving improvements in indoor environmental quality. Employees' salaries are a significant cost in any commercial building, so it makes good business sense to keep staff healthy and productive.

For schools, indoor environmental quality has a significant effect on the health and well-being of students and staff, as well as on the quality and effectiveness of the learning environment. Compared with adults, children are at greater risk of exposure to and possible illness from environmental hazards because of their greater sensitivity during development and growth. Continuous exposure to hazardous substances can lead to learning disabilities, cancers, and illnesses caused by damage to the nervous system.

LEED Green Building Rating Systems aim to provide optimal indoor environmental quality through the careful use of technologies and strategies that improve building system effectiveness and occupant productivity. For example, credits in the IEQ category encourage automatic sensors and individual controls that allow users to adjust temperature, humidity, and ventilation based on individual preference.

Additional indoor environmental quality issues addressed by LEED for New Construction, Core & Shell, and Schools cover access to daylight, lighting quality, ventilation, thermal comfort, acoustics, and access to views. These issues all have the potential to enhance the indoor environment and optimize interior spaces for building occupants.

SYNERGIES

Two overarching concepts are addressed in this category—maintaining high-quality indoor air and providing a high level of occupant comfort. Within each of these two concepts are multiple specific strategies, such as providing access to daylight (occupant comfort) and specifying low-emitting flooring systems (air quality). While they may seem disconnected, they actually work together to maintain a healthy and productive indoor environment, and both concepts focus on the building occupant. For example, poor daylight design may cause glare and unwanted heat gain, which would make a space thermally and visually uncomfortable. From another perspective, many interior materials and finishes contain odorous, irritating, and/or harmful contaminants that off-gas inside the building and continue to do so long after they are installed.

Additionally, the credits in this category may have a large impact on energy consumption. Occupant thermal comfort, ventilation rate, and air filtration often depend on mechanical systems. When a project includes occupant controls for lighting and thermal comfort, the project team will need to

INDOOR ENVIRONMENTAL QUALITY

work together to assess how the controls could affect energy consumption. Furthermore, the team will need to work with suppliers, contractors, and the commissioning agent to ensure that the systems are installed and functioning as intended.

As you study, consider the synergies related to the Energy and Atmosphere category and the Materials and Resources category.

CATEGORY HIGHLIGHTS

- Several referenced standards are used within the Indoor Environmental Quality category. Make sure you pay attention to these standards and can remember which standard is associated with each credit.

- LEED projects must achieve minimum ventilation rates. Additional credit is awarded for projects that sufficiently exceed this minimum level.

- Acoustics and mold prevention are of special concern within schools. This is reflected in the LEED 2009 for Schools–only prerequisite and credits, IEQ Prerequisite 3, Minimum Acoustical Performance; IEQ Credit 9, Enhanced Acoustical Performance; and IEQ Credit 10, Mold Prevention.

- Construction activities and the specification of building materials have lasting effects on the indoor air quality of the building. Careful selection of low-emitting materials and conscientious construction practices are recognized in this category.

- Providing occupant controllability, access to views and daylight, increased ventilation, and superior thermal comfort are all specifically considered within this category.

INDOOR ENVIRONMENTAL QUALITY

INDOOR ENVIRONMENTAL QUALITY CREDITS

IEQ

CREDIT	TITLE	NC	SCHOOLS	CS
IEQ Prerequisite 1	Minimum Indoor Air Quality Performance	Required	Required	Required
IEQ Prerequisite 2	Environmental Tobacco Smoke (ETS) Control	Required	Required	Required
IEQ Prerequisite 3	Minimum Acoustical Performance	N/A	Required	N/A
IEQ Credit 1	Outdoor Air Delivery Monitoring	1 point	1 point	1 point
IEQ Credit 2	Increased Ventilation	1 point	1 point	1 point
IEQ Credit 3.1	Construction Indoor Air Quality Management Plan During Construction	1 point	1 point	NA
IEQ Credit 3	Construction Indoor Air Quality Management Plan During Construction	N/A	N/A	1 point
IEQ Credit 3.2	Construction Indoor Air Quality Management Plan Before Occupancy	1 point	1 point	NA
IEQ Credit 4.1	Low-Emitting Materials—Adhesives and Sealants	1 point	1 point	1 point
IEQ Credit 4.2	Low-Emitting Materials—Paints and Coatings	1 point	1 point	1 point
IEQ Credit 4.3	Low-Emitting Materials—Flooring Systems	1 point	1 point	1 point
IEQ Credit 4.4	Low-Emitting Materials—Composite Wood and Agrifiber Products	1 point	1 point	1 point
IEQ Credit 4.5	Low-Emitting Materials—Furniture and Furnishings	N/A	1 point	N/A
IEQ Credit 4.6	Low-Emitting Materials—Ceiling and Wall Systems	NA	1 point	NA
IEQ Credit 5	Indoor Chemical and Pollutant Source Control	1 point	1 point	1 point
IEQ Credit 6.1	Controllability of Systems—Lighting	1 point	1 point	N/A
IEQ Credit 6.2	Controllability of Systems—Thermal Comfort	1 point	1 point	NA
IEQ Credit 6	Controllability of Systems—Thermal Comfort	N/A	N/A	1 point
IEQ Credit 7.1	Thermal Comfort—Design	1 point	1 point	N/A
IEQ Credit 7	Thermal Comfort—Design	N/A	N/A	1 point
IEQ Credit 7.2	Thermal Comfort—Verification	1 point	1 point	N/A
IEQ Credit 8.1	Daylight and Views—Daylight	1 point	1-3 points	1 point
IEQ Credit 8.2	Daylight and Views—Views	1 point	1 points	1 point
IEQ Credit 9	Enhanced Acoustical Performance	N/A	1 point	N/A
IEQ Credit 10	Mold Prevention	N/A	1 point	N/A

KEY TERMS

Adhesive	Any substance used to bond one surface to another by attachment. Adhesives include bonding primers, adhesive primers, and adhesive primers for plastics. (SCAQMD Rule 1168)
Aerosol adhesive	An aerosol product in which the spray mechanism is permanently housed in a nonrefillable can. Designed for hand-held application, these products do not need ancillary hoses or spray equipment. Aerosol adhesives include special-purpose spray adhesives, mist spray adhesives, and web spray adhesives. (SCAQMD Rule 1168)
Agrifiber products	Products made from agricultural fiber. Examples include particleboard, medium-density fiberboard (MDF), plywood, oriented-strand board (OSB), wheatboard, and strawboard.
Anticorrosive paints	Coatings formulated and recommended for use in preventing the corrosion of ferrous metal substrates.
Architectural porous sealant	A substance used as a sealant on porous materials.
Audiovisual (A/V)	Slides, film, video, sound recordings, and the devices used to present such media.
Building envelope	The entire outer shell of a building, including areas of walls, floors and ceilings.
Carbon dioxide (CO$_2$) levels	An indicator of ventilation effectiveness inside buildings. CO$_2$ concentrations greater than 530 ppm above outdoor CO$_2$ conditions generally indicate inadequate ventilation. Absolute concentrations of CO$_2$ greater than 800 to 1,000 ppm generally indicate poor air quality for breathing.
Coating	A coating is applied to beautify, protect, or provide a barrier to a surface. Flat coatings register a gloss of less than 15 on an 85-degree meter or less than 5 on a 60-degree meter. Nonflat coatings register a gloss of 5 or greater on a 60-degree meter and a gloss of 15 or greater on an 85-degree meter. (SCAQMD Rule 1113)
Comfort criteria	Specific design conditions that take into account temperature, humidity, air speed, outdoor temperature, outdoor humidity, seasonal clothing, and expected activity. (ASHRAE 55–2004)

Composite wood	Wood or plant particles or fibers bonded by a synthetic resin or binder. Examples include particleboard, medium-density fiberboard (MDF), plywood, oriented-strand board (OSB), wheatboard, and strawboard.
Contaminants	Unwanted airborne elements that may reduce indoor air quality. (ASHRAE 62.1– 2007)
Controls	Mechanisms that allow occupants to direct power to devices (such as lights and heaters) or adjust devices or systems within a range (such as brightness and temperature).
Core learning spaces	Areas for educational activities where the primary functions are teaching and learning. (ANSI S12.60–2002)
Densely occupied space	An area with a design occupant density of 25 people or more per 1,000 square feet (40 square feet or less per person).
Environmental tobacco smoke (ETS)	Also known as secondhand smoke, it consists of airborne particles emitted from the burning end of cigarettes, pipes, and cigars and is exhaled by smokers. These particles contain about 4,000 compounds, up to 50 of which are known to cause cancer.
Footcandle (fc)	A measure of light falling on a given surface. One footcandle is defined as the quantity of light falling on a 1 square-foot area from a 1 candela light source at a distance of 1 foot (which equals 1 lumen per square foot). Footcandles can be measured both horizontally and vertically by a footcandle meter or light meter.
Formaldehyde	A naturally occurring VOC found in small amounts in animals and plants but is carcinogenic and an irritant to most people when present in high concentrations, causing headaches, dizziness, mental impairment, and other symptoms. When present in the air at levels above 0.1 ppm, it can cause watery eyes; burning sensations in the eyes, nose, and throat; nausea; coughing; chest tightness; wheezing; skin rashes; and asthmatic and allergic reactions.
Group (shared) multi-occupant spaces	Conference rooms, classrooms, and other indoor spaces used as places of congregation.
HVAC systems	Equipment, distribution systems, and terminals that provide the processes of heating, ventilating, or air conditioning. (ASHRAE 90.1– 2007)

Individual occupant spaces	Standard workstations where workers conduct individual tasks.
Indoor adhesive, sealant, or sealant primer	An adhesive or sealant product applied on-site, inside the building's weatherproofing system.
Indoor air quality (IAQ)	The nature of air inside the space that affects the health and well-being of building occupants. It is considered acceptable when there are no known contaminants at harmful concentrations and a substantial majority (80% or more) of the occupants do not express dissatisfaction. (ASHRAE 62.1–2007)
Mechanical ventilation, or active ventilation	Ventilation provided by mechanically powered equipment, such as motor-driven fans and blowers, but not by devices such as wind-driven turbine ventilators and mechanically operated windows. (ASHRAE 62.1–2004)
Minimum efficiency reporting value (MERV)	A filter rating established by the American Society of Heating, Refrigerating and Air-Conditioning Engineers (ASHRAE 52.2–1999, Method of Testing General Ventilation Air-Cleaning Devices for Removal Efficiency by Particle Size). MERV categories range from 1 (very low efficiency) to 16 (very high efficiency).
Mixed-mode ventilation	A combination of mechanical and natural ventilation methods.
Natural ventilation, or passive ventilation	Includes thermal, wind, or diffusion effects through doors, windows, or other intentional openings in the building; it uses the building layout, fabric, and form to achieve heat transfer and air movement.
Noise reduction coefficient (NRC)	The arithmetic average of absorption coefficients at 250, 500, 1,000, and 2,000 Hz for a material. The NRC is often published by manufacturers in product specifications, particularly for acoustical ceiling tiles and acoustical wall panels.
Nonoccupied spaces	All rooms used by maintenance personnel that are not open for use by occupants. Examples are closets and janitorial, storage, and equipment rooms.
Nonporous sealant	A substance used as a sealant on nonporous materials. Nonporous materials, such as plastic and metal, do not have openings in which fluids may be absorbed or discharged.

Occupants	In a commercial building, occupants are workers who either have a permanent office or workstation in the building or typically spend a minimum of 10 hours per week in the building. In a residential building, occupants also include all persons who live in the building. In schools, occupants also include students, faculty, support staff, administrators, and maintenance employees.
Off-gassing	The emission of volatile organic compounds (VOCs) from synthetic and natural products.
Outdoor air	The ambient air that enters a building through a ventilation system, either through natural ventilation or by infiltration. (ASHRAE 62.1–2007)
Ozone (O_3)	A gas composed of three oxygen atoms. It is not usually emitted directly into the air, but at ground level it is created by a chemical reaction between oxides of nitrogen (NOx) and volatile organic compounds (VOCs) in the presence of sunlight. Ozone has the same chemical structure whether it occurs in the atmosphere or at ground level and can have positive or negative effects, depending on its location. (U.S. Environmental Protection Agency)
Phenol formaldehyde	A chemical that off-gasses only at high temperatures, it is used for exterior products, although many of these products are suitable for interior applications.
Porous materials	Materials with tiny openings, often microscopic, that can absorb or discharge fluids. Examples include wood, fabric, paper, corrugated paperboard, and plastic foam. (SCAQMD Rule 1168)
Regularly occupied spaces	Areas where workers are seated or standing as they work inside a building. In residential applications, these areas are all spaces except bathrooms, utility areas, and closets or other storage rooms. In schools, they are areas where students, teachers, or administrators are seated or standing as they work or study inside a building.
Relative humidity	The ratio of partial density of airborne water vapor to the saturation density of water vapor at the same temperature and total pressure.
Reverberation	An acoustical phenomenon that occurs when sound persists in an enclosed space because of its repeated reflection or scattering on the enclosing surfaces or objects within the space. (ANSI S12.60–2002)

Reverberation time (RT)	A measure of the amount of reverberation in a space and equal to the time required for the level of a steady sound to decay by 60 dB after the sound has stopped. The decay rate depends on the amount of sound absorption in a room, the room geometry, and the frequency of the sound. RT is expressed in seconds. (ANSI S12.60–2002)
Sound absorption	The portion of sound energy striking a surface that is not returned as sound energy. (ANSI S12.60–2002)
Sound absorption coefficient	The ability of a material to absorb sound, expressed as a fraction of incident sound. The sound absorption coefficient is frequency specific and ranges from 0.00 to 1.00. For example, a material may have an absorption coefficient of 0.50 at 250 Hz and 0.80 at 1,000 Hz. This indicates that the material absorbs 50% of incident sound at 250 Hz and 80% of incident sound at 1,000 Hz. The arithmetic average of absorption coefficients at midfrequencies is the noise reduction coefficient.
Sound transmission class (STC)	A single-number rating for the acoustic attenuation of airborne sound passing through a partition or other building element, such as a wall, roof, or door, as measured in an acoustical testing laboratory according to accepted industry practice. A higher STC rating provides more sound attenuation through a partition. (ANSI S12.60–2002)
Thermal comfort	When occupants express satisfaction with the thermal environment.
Urea formaldehyde	A combination of urea and formaldehyde that is used in some glues and may emit formaldehyde at room temperature.
Ventilation	The process of supplying air to or removing air from a space for the purpose of controlling air contaminant levels, humidity, or temperature within the space. (ASHRAE 62.1–2007).
Visible light transmittance (VLT) (Tvis)	The ratio of total transmitted light to total incident light (that is, the amount of visible spectrum, 380–780 nanometers of light passing through a glazing surface divided by the amount of light striking the glazing surface). The higher the Tvis value, the more incident light passes through the glazing.
Vision glazing	The portion of an exterior window between 30 and 90 inches above the floor that permits a view to the outside.

Volatile organic compounds (VOCs)	Carbon compounds that participate in atmospheric photochemical reactions (excluding carbon monoxide, carbon dioxide, carbonic acid, metallic carbides and carbonates, and ammonium carbonate). The compounds vaporize (become a gas) at normal room temperatures.
Weighted decibel (dBA)	A sound pressure level measured with a conventional frequency weighting that roughly approximates how the human ear hears different frequency components of sounds at typical listening levels for speech. (ANSI S12.60–2002)

NC: Required
Schools: Required
CS: Required

IEQ Prerequisite 1: Minimum Indoor Air Quality Performance

NC: 1 Point
Schools: 1 Point
CS: 1 Point

IEQ Credit 2: Increased Ventilation

KEY TERMS

VENTILATION

MECHANICAL VENTILATION

NATURAL VENTILATION

MIXED-MODE VENTILATION

OUTDOOR AIR

INDOOR AIR QUALITY (IAQ)

RELATED CREDITS

SS Credit 3: Brownfield Redevelopment

SS Credit 4: Alternative Transportation

EA Prerequisite 1: Fundamental Commissioning

EA Credit 3: Enhanced Commissioning

EA Credit 5: Measurement and Verification

IEQ Prerequisite 2: Environmental Tobacco Smoke (ETS) Control

IEQ Credits 4: Low-Emitting Materials

IEQ Credit 5: Indoor Chemical and Pollutant Source Control

INTENT

IEQ Prerequisite 1:

To establish minimum and increased indoor air quality (IAQ) performance to enhance indoor air quality in buildings, thus contributing to the health and well-being of the occupants.

IEQ Credit 2:

To provide additional outdoor air ventilation to improve IAQ and promote occupant comfort, well-being, and productivity.

REQUIREMENTS

For mechanically ventilated spaces:

IEQ Prerequisite 1:

Modify or maintain each outside air intake, supply an air fan and/or ventilation distribution system to supply at least the outdoor air ventilation rate required by ASHRAE Standard 62.1–2007 or local code, whichever is more stringent.

IEQ Credit 2:

Increase the outdoor air supply to exceed the prerequisite requirements by at least 30%.

For naturally ventilated spaces:

IEQ Prerequisite 1:

Comply with ASHRAE Standard 62.1–2007, Paragraph 5.1.

IEQ Credit 2:

Design the system to meet the recommendations of the Carbon Trust's "Good Practice Guide 237." Additionally, follow the flow diagram process shown in Figure 1.18 of the CIBSE Applications Manual 10–2005, Natural Ventilation in Non-Domestic Buildings. Finally, show that the natural ventilation will be effective by using diagrams and calculations (showing that the design meets the requirements of CIBSE Applications Manual 10: 2005), or provide analytic modeling to demonstrate compliance with ASHRAE 62.1–2007, Chapter 6, in at least 90% of spaces.

IEQ Prerequisite 1: Minimum Indoor Air Quality Performance

 No

IEQ Credit 2: Increased Ventilation

Exemplary Performance

 No

IMPLEMENTATION

Design the building to meet the minimum required ventilation rates for mechanically ventilated, naturally ventilated, and mixed-mode ventilated spaces based on the referenced standard(s).

- Mechanically ventilated spaces should use the ventilation rate procedure detailed in ASHRAE 62.1–2007.
- Naturally ventilated spaces should use ASHRAE Standard 62.1–2007, Paragraph 5.1.
- Mixed-mode ventilated spaces should meet the minimum ventilation rates required by Chapter 6 of ASHRAE 62.1–2007.

Projects pursuing IEQ Credit 2, Increased Ventilation, must provide an additional 30% outdoor air to all spaces with mechanical ventilation (including mixed mode). Spaces without mechanical ventilation (naturally ventilated) must be designed to meet the Carbon Trust's "Good Practice Guide 237."

DOCUMENTATION & CALCULATIONS

The mechanical designer should develop ventilation calculations demonstrating compliance with the applicable sections of ASHRAE 62.1–2007 and, where required, create diagrams and calculations or an analytic model to confirm natural ventilation effectiveness.

NOTES

When local code is more stringent, it should be used in lieu of ASHRAE 62.1–2007.

Mechanical ventilation systems installed in LEED 2009 for Core & Shell projects must be sufficient to meet future tenant ventilation needs.

TIME LINE/TEAM

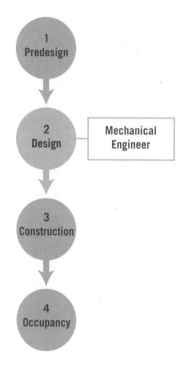

1 Predesign

2 Design — Mechanical Engineer

3 Construction

4 Occupancy

STANDARDS

ASHRAE Standard 62.1–2007, Ventilation for Acceptable Indoor Air Quality

CIBSE Applications Manual 10–2005, Natural Ventilation in Non-Domestic Buildings

IEQ Prerequisite 2:
Environmental Tobacco Smoke (ETS) Control

KEY TERMS

ENVIRONMENTAL TOBACCO SMOKE

VENTILATION

RELATED CREDITS

EA Prerequisite 1:
Fundamental Commissioning

EA Credit 1: Optimize Energy
Performance

EA Credit 3: Enhanced
Commissioning

EA Credit 5: Measurement and
Verification

IEQ Prerequisite 1: Minimum
Indoor Air Quality Performance

IEQ Credit 1: Outdoor Air
Delivery Monitoring

IEQ Credit 2: Increased
Ventilation

INTENT

NC and CS:

To prevent or minimize exposure of building occupants, indoor surfaces, and ventilation air distribution systems to environmental tobacco smoke (ETS).

Schools:

To eliminate exposure of building occupants, indoor surfaces, and ventilation air distribution systems to ETS.

REQUIREMENTS

- Prohibit smoking in the building. LEED for New Construction or LEED for Core & Shell may alternatively provide designated smoking rooms designed to mitigate the impacts of indoor smoking.

- Prohibit smoking within 25 feet of all operable windows, doors, and air intakes.

- For residential and hospitality projects, in addition to the above requirements, tightly seal all penetrations and adjacent vertical chases in residential units to control ETS transfer between units, and weather-strip all doors leading to common hallways and windows and doors to the building exterior to control ETS transfer to common areas. Conduct blower door testing to demonstrate that the units are sufficiently sealed.

IMPLEMENTATION

For all projects, prohibit smoking within the building.

Post signage designating smoking and nonsmoking areas and ensure that the 25-foot setback requirements are met for all doors, operable windows, and building air intakes.

If smoking areas exist within the building, install separate and isolated ventilation systems.

IMPLEMENTATION, CONTINUED

Residential and hospitality projects that allow smoking should protect other tenants from the resulting environmental tobacco smoke by doing the following:

- Choose very tight construction;

- Seal any penetrations in walls, ceilings, and floors in each residential unit;

- Seal all vertical chases adjacent to units;

- Weather-strip all exterior doors and operable windows and in the residential units leading to common areas; and

- Conduct blower door testing according to the referenced standards.

DOCUMENTATION & CALCULATIONS

Develop an environmental tobacco smoke policy and maintain site plans or similar documents that show where smoking is prohibited.

NOTES

The relationship between smoking and various health risks, including lung disease, cancer, and heart disease, is well documented. A strong link between ETS and similar health risks has also been demonstrated.

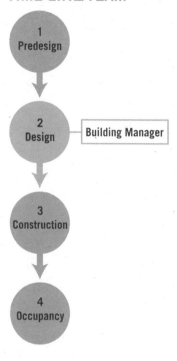

TIME LINE/TEAM

1 Predesign

2 Design — Building Manager

3 Construction

4 Occupancy

STANDARDS

ANSI/ASTM-E779–03, Standard Test Method for Determining Air Leakage Rate by Fan Pressurization

Residential Manual for Compliance with California's 2001 Energy Efficiency Standards (for Low Rise Residential Buildings), Chapter 4

NC: N/A
Schools: Required
CS: N/A

IEQ Prerequisite 3: Minimum Acoustical Performance (Schools)

NC: N/A
Schools: 1 Point
CS: N/A

IEQ Credit 9: Enhanced Acoustical Performance (Schools)

KEY TERMS

BUILDING ENVELOPE

CORE LEARNING SPACES

HVAC SYSTEMS

NOISE REDUCTION COEFFICIENT (NRC)

REVERBERATION TIME (RT)

SOUND TRANSMISSION CLASS (STC)

WEIGHTED DECIBEL (DBA)

INTENT

IEQ Prerequisite 3:

To provide classrooms that are quiet so that teachers can speak to the class without straining their voices and students can effectively communicate with each other and the teacher.

IEQ Credit 9:

To provide classrooms that facilitate better teacher-to-student and student-to-student communication through effective acoustical design.

RELATED CREDITS

None

REQUIREMENTS

IEQ Prerequisite 3:

Meet the reverberation time (RT) requirements of ANSI Standard S12.60–2002, Acoustical Performance Criteria, in all core learning spaces.

Design HVAC systems that do not exceed 45 dBA in all core learning spaces.

For small core learning spaces (less than 20,000 cubic feet), ceiling areas (excluding lights, diffusers, and grilles) must have a noise reduction coefficient (NRC) of 0.70 or higher. Alternatively, a combined area of ceiling and other interior surfaces equal to or greater than the ceiling area (excluding lights, diffusers, and grilles) must have an NRC of 0.70 or higher.

For large core learning spaces (equal to or greater than 20,000 cubic feet), confirm via ANSI Standard S12.60–2002 that the RT is 1.5 seconds or less.

IEQ Credit 9:

Meet the sound transmission class (STC) requirements of ANSI Standard S12.60–2002 for building shells and partitions within core learning spaces. Windows within core learning spaces must have an STC of at least 35.

Design HVAC systems that do not exceed 40 dBA in all core learning spaces.

IMPLEMENTATION

Design all classrooms and other core learning spaces to have low background noise and a short reverberation time.

Select wall assemblies that meet the STC requirements.

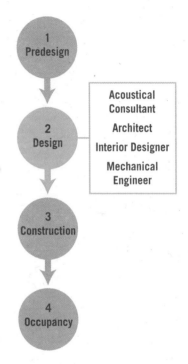

TIME LINE/TEAM

1 Predesign

2 Design — Acoustical Consultant, Architect, Interior Designer, Mechanical Engineer

3 Construction

4 Occupancy

DOCUMENTATION & CALCULATIONS

Retain manufacturer information indicating acoustical information and drawings that show the areas of installation, to confirm the NRC requirements. Calculations regarding the background noise from HVAC systems, and confirmation of the reverberation times, should also be retained.

Acoustical engineering calculations are used to determine the total sound absorption and reverberation times. In order to calculate the RT of a room, you will need the following information:

● Volume (in cubic feet);

● Interior surface area (in square feet);

● Sound absorption coefficients at frequencies of 500, 1,000, and 2,000 Hz for each interior fixed element; and

● Surface area of each interior fixed element.

Maintain records of ratings and treatments used for sound control as well as the means by which the project team has met the requirements of the referenced standard.

STANDARDS

ANSI Standard S12.60–2002, Acoustical Performance Criteria, Design Requirements, and Guidelines for Schools

ASHRAE Handbook, Chapter 47, Sound and Vibration Control, 2003 HVAC Applications

NOTES

This prerequisite addresses RT, background noise, and interior surfaces for rooms less than 20,000 cubic feet, and has additional RT requirements for rooms 20,000 cubic feet or greater. IEQ Credit 9, Enhanced Acoustical Performance, goes beyond this to include lower background noise levels and sound transmission classes (STCs).

NC: 1 Point
Schools: 1 Point
CS: 1 Point

IEQ Credit 1:
Outdoor Air Delivery Monitoring

KEY TERMS

CARBON DIOXIDE (CO2) LEVELS

DENSELY OCCUPIED SPACE

HVAC SYSTEMS

INDOOR AIR QUALITY (IAQ)

MECHANICAL VENTILATION

NATURAL VENTILATION

OCCUPANTS

OUTDOOR AIR

VENTILATION

RELATED CREDITS

 IEQ Credit 2: Increased Ventilation

EA Prerequisite 1: Fundamental Commissioning

EA Credit 3: Enhanced Commissioning

EA Credit 5: Measurement and Verification

SS Credit 4: Alternative Transportation

INTENT

To provide capacity for ventilation system monitoring to help promote occupant comfort and well-being.

REQUIREMENTS

Install CO_2 sensors that sound an alarm when CO_2 values vary by 10% or more from the design values. For densely occupied mechanically ventilated spaces and all naturally ventilated spaces, monitor CO_2 concentrations within all spaces. For ventilation systems that serve nondensely occupied spaces, install outdoor air intake measuring devices.

● CO_2 sensors must be located within the area we breathe (the breathing zone): 3 to 6 feet above the floor.

IMPLEMENTATION

Monitor the outdoor airflow rate as a way to confirm that HVAC equipment is providing the required ventilation rate.

CO_2 monitoring should be applied to both densely occupied mechanically ventilated and all naturally ventilated spaces.

Core & Shell projects can consider including CO_2 sensors in tenant spaces.

164   USGBC LEED AP Building Design + Construction Study Guide

IEQ Credit 1:
Outdoor Air Delivery Monitoring

DOCUMENTATION & CALCULATIONS

Document the CO_2 sensors and/or airflow monitors on project drawings, indicating location, and in mechanical schedules.

Incorporate the systems into the commissioning process.

NOTES

HVAC systems are designed to flush out indoor airborne contaminants, so why wouldn't we want to monitor them?

Nondensely occupied spaces are defined as having fewer than 25 people per 1,000 square feet.

TIME LINE/TEAM

1 Predesign

2 Design — Mechanical Engineer

3 Construction

4 Occupancy

STANDARDS

ASHRAE 62.1–2007, Ventilation for Acceptable Indoor Air Quality

NC: 1 Point
Schools: 1 Point
CS: 1 Point

IEQ Credit 3.1: Construction IAQ Management Plan, During Construction (NC & Schools)
IEQ Credit 3: Construction IAQ Management Plan, During Construction (CS)

KEY TERMS

HVAC SYSTEMS

INDOOR AIR QUALITY (IAQ)

MINIMUM EFFICIENCY REPORTING VALUE (MERV)

RELATED CREDITS

 IEQ Credit 3.2: Construction Indoor Air Quality Management Plan – Before Occupancy

 IEQ Credit 4: Low-Emitting Materials

 IEQ Credit 5: Indoor Chemical and Pollutant Source Control

INTENT

To reduce indoor air quality (IAQ) problems resulting from construction or renovation and promote the comfort and well-being of construction workers and building occupants.

REQUIREMENTS

Create an IAQ management plan for the construction and preoccupancy phases.

During construction, meet or exceed the Sheet Metal and Air Conditioning Contractors National Association's control measures.

Protect stored on-site or installed absorptive materials from moisture damage.

If permanently installed air handlers are used during construction, MERV 8 filtration media must be used at each return air grille. Replace all filtration media immediately prior to occupancy.

For LEED for Schools projects, smoking must be prohibited inside the building and within 25 feet of building entrances once the building is enclosed.

IMPLEMENTATION

Create an IAQ management plan to guide the construction and preoccupancy IAQ management practices. Educate and review the plan with subcontractors and field personnel to ensure implementation.

The IAQ management plan should address the following:

- Storage of construction materials in order to avoid moisture damage;
- Installation of filters if air handlers will be used during construction;
- HVAC protection;
- Source control;
- Pathway interruption;
- Housekeeping; and
- Scheduling.

Exemplary Performance

No

DOCUMENTATION & CALCULATIONS

Develop a construction indoor air quality management plan.

Take photos to log IAQ management plan practices.

NOTES

Building construction has the potential to introduce contaminants such as dust into the building. If unaddressed, the contamination can result in poor indoor air quality extending over the lifetime of the building.

LEED for Schools projects must begin enforcement of IEQ Prerequisite 2, Environmental Tobacco Smoke (ETS) Control, as soon as the building is enclosed.

TIME LINE/TEAM

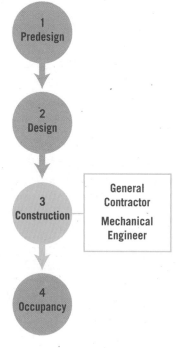

STANDARDS

Sheet Metal and Air Conditioning Contractors National Association (SMACNA) IAQ Guidelines for Occupied Buildings Under Construction, 2nd Edition 2007, ANSI/SMACNA 008-2008 (Chapter 3)

ANSI/ASHRAE Standard 52.2–1999: Method of Testing General Ventilation Air-Cleaning Devices for Removal Efficiency by Particle Size

IEQ Credit 3.2: Construction IAQ Management Plan, Before Occupancy (NC and Schools Only)

KEY TERMS

CONTAMINANTS

HVAC SYSTEMS

INDOOR AIR QUALITY (IAQ)

OUTDOOR AIR

RELATED CREDITS

 IEQ Prerequisite 1: Minimum Indoor Air Quality Performance

 IEQ Credit 2: Increased Ventilation

 IEQ Credit 3.1: Construction Indoor Air Quality Management Plan – During Construction

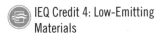 IEQ Credit 4: Low-Emitting Materials

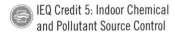 IEQ Credit 5: Indoor Chemical and Pollutant Source Control

INTENT

To reduce indoor air quality (IAQ) problems resulting from any construction or renovation projects to promote the comfort and well-being of construction workers and building occupants.

REQUIREMENTS

Complete a building flush-out to remove contaminants, or conduct air quality testing to confirm that contaminants are below allowable levels.

Flush-Out:

Conduct a flush-out that supplies 14,000 cubic feet of outside air per square foot to the project interior. If occupancy is desired prior to completion, the space may be occupied after 3,500 cubic feet of outside air per square foot have been delivered, as long as acceptable minimum ventilation rates are maintained until the full flush-out (14,000 cubic feet per square foot) has been completed.

IAQ Testing:

Conduct air quality testing prior to occupancy to confirm that indoor air contaminants are within the following thresholds:

Contaminant	Maximum Concentration
Formaldehyde	27 parts per billion
Particulates (PM10)	50 micrograms per cubic meter
Total volatile organic compounds (TVOCs)	500 micrograms per cubic meter
4-Phenylcyclohexene (4-PCH)*	6.5 micrograms per cubic meter
Carbon monoxide (CO)	9 parts per million and no greater than 2 parts per million above outdoor levels

*This test is required only if carpets and fabrics with styrene butadiene rubber (SBR) latex backing are installed as part of the base building systems.

IMPLEMENTATION

Complete all construction-related and cleaning activities prior to flush-out or air quality testing.

Flush-Out Procedure:

- Install new filtration media and flush out the space.

- Supply a total outdoor air volume of 14,000 cubic feet per square foot of floor area while maintaining an internal temperature of at least 60 F and maintaining a relative humidity no higher than 60%.

IMPLEMENTATION, CONTINUED

- The space may be occupied after at least 3,500 cubic feet of outdoor air per square foot of floor area have been delivered and the space has been ventilated at a minimum rate of 0.30 cfm per square foot of outdoor air or the design minimum outside air rate (whichever is greater).
  - ○ Continue the flush-out until a total of 14,000 cubic feet per square foot of outdoor air has been delivered to the space.
- The flush-out may continue during occupancy.

Air Quality Testing:

- This approach confirms that major contaminants are below the acceptable level.
- Avoid substitutions for low-emitting materials.
- Use low-VOC cleaning supplies.
- Use vacuum cleaners with HEPA filters.
- Use the protocol outlined in the referenced standard.
  - ○ Select appropriate sampling locations.
  - ○ Take at least one sample per 25,000 square feet.
  - ○ Take samples in the breathing zone and during normal occupied hours.
- Record exact sample locations in case retesting is required.
- Pass the test! If you don't, flush out the space and retest.
  - ○ Retesting may be limited to only those contaminants that exceed the maximum levels.

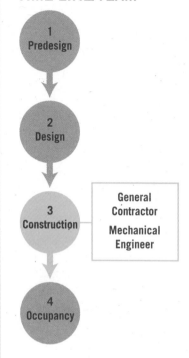

TIME LINE/TEAM

1 Predesign

2 Design

3 Construction — General Contractor / Mechanical Engineer

4 Occupancy

STANDARDS

U.S. Environmental Protection Agency Compendium of Methods for the Determination of Air Pollutants in Indoor Air

DOCUMENTATION & CALCULATIONS

For projects completing a flush-out procedure, record the procedures, including start date and time. Confirm how humidity and temperature requirements will be met.

For projects completing air quality testing, record the testing procedures, including the sampling locations. Document the air contaminant values as measured.

NOTES

Building construction has the potential to introduce contaminants into the building. To prevent poor indoor air quality over the lifetime of the building, institute IAQ management strategies to minimize them.

IEQ Credit 4.1: Low-Emitting Materials, Adhesives and Sealants

KEY TERMS

ADHESIVE

AEROSOL ADHESIVE

CONTAMINANTS

INDOOR AIR QUALITY (IAQ)

OCCUPANTS

OFF-GASSING

VOLATILE ORGANIC COMPOUNDS (VOCS)

RELATED CREDITS

IEQ Prerequisite 2: Environmental Tobacco Smoke (ETS) Control

IEQ Prerequisite 3: Minimum Acoustical Performance (Schools only)

IEQ Credit 3.1: Construction IAQ Management Plan – During Construction

IEQ Credit 3.2: Construction IAQ Management Plan ¬– Before Occupancy

IEQ Credit 4.2: Low-Emitting Materials – Paints and Coatings

IEQ Credit 4.3: Low-Emitting Materials – Flooring Systems

IEQ Credit 4.4: Low-Emitting Materials – Composite Wood and Agrifiber Products

IEQ Credit 4.5: Low-Emitting Materials – Furniture and Furnishings (Schools only)

IEQ Credit 4.6: Low-Emitting Materials – Ceiling and Wall Systems (Schools only)

IEQ Credit 5: Indoor Chemical and Pollutant Source Control

IEQ Credit 9: Enhanced Acoustical Performance (Schools only)

INTENT

To reduce the quantity of indoor air contaminants that are odorous, irritating, and/or harmful to the comfort and well-being of installers and occupants.

REQUIREMENTS

NC and CS:

Adhesives, sealants, and sealant primers installed in the building interior must comply with South Coast Air Quality Management District (SCAQMD) Rule 1168.

Aerosol adhesives must comply with the Green Seal Standard for Commercial Adhesives GS-36 requirements.

Schools:

All adhesives and sealants installed in the building interior must meet the testing and product requirements of the California Department of Health Services Standard Practice for the Testing of Volatile Organic Emissions from Various Sources Using Small-Scale Environmental Chambers, including 2004 Addenda.

IMPLEMENTATION

- Include VOC limits or identify specific products within the project specifications.

- For LEED for Schools projects, specify only those materials that meet the requirements of the referenced standard.

DOCUMENTATION & CALCULATIONS

Track all indoor aerosol adhesive products, adhesives, sealants, and sealant primers used in the project.

The VOC budget methodology compares the design case with a baseline case in order to demonstrate that the overall low-VOC performance has been attained. When the design is less than the baseline, the credit requirement is satisfied. If a product with higher than allowable VOC content is used, follow the VOC budget approach to determine whether the credit can still be achieved.

NOTES

The VOC threshold limits and content are generally expressed in grams per liter (g/L).

Schools projects may choose from IEQ Credits 4.1–4.6, Low-Emitting Materials, for a maximum of four points.

Per the USGBC Performance/Intent Equivalent Alternative Compliance Path (PIEACP) dated July 7, 2008, LEED for Schools projects may substitute the LEED for New Construction v2.2 credit requirements in place of the LEED for Schools requirements for this credit.

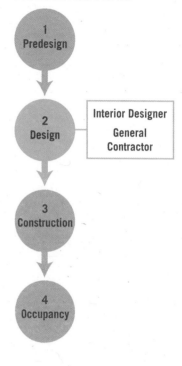

TIME LINE/TEAM

1 Predesign

2 Design — Interior Designer / General Contractor

3 Construction

4 Occupancy

STANDARDS

NC and CS:

South Coast Air Quality Management District (SCAQMD) Amendment to South Coast Rule 1168, VOC Limits, effective January 7, 2005

Green Seal Standard 36 (GS-36), effective October 19, 2000

Schools:

California Department of Health Services Standard Practice for the Testing of Volatile Organic Emissions from Various Sources Using Small-Scale Environmental Chambers, including 2004 Addenda

IEQ Credit 4.2: Low-Emitting Materials, Paints and Coatings

KEY TERMS

ANTICORROSIVE PAINTS

COATING

CONTAMINANTS

INDOOR AIR QUALITY (IAQ)

OCCUPANTS

VOLATILE ORGANIC COMPOUNDS (VOCS)

RELATED CREDITS

IEQ Prerequisite 2: Environmental Tobacco Smoke (ETS) Control

IEQ Prerequisite 3: Minimum Acoustical Performance (Schools only)

IEQ Credit 3.1: Construction IAQ Management Plan – During Construction

IEQ Credit 3.2: Construction IAQ Management Plan – Before Occupancy

IEQ Credit 4.1: Low-Emitting Materials – Adhesives and Sealants

IEQ Credit 4.3: Low-Emitting Materials – Flooring Systems

IEQ Credit 4.4: Low-Emitting Materials – Composite Wood and Agrifiber Products

IEQ Credit 4.5: Low-Emitting Materials – Furniture and Furnishings (Schools only)

IEQ Credit 4.6: Low-Emitting Materials – Ceiling and Wall Systems (Schools only)

IEQ Credit 5: Indoor Chemical and Pollutant Source Control

IEQ Credit 9: Enhanced Acoustical Performance (Schools only)

INTENT

To reduce the quantity of indoor air contaminants that are odorous, irritating, and/or harmful to the comfort and well-being of installers and occupants.

REQUIREMENTS

NC and CS:

Paints and coatings used in the building interior must meet the following conditions:

- Architectural paints and coatings must comply with Green Seal Standard GS-11.
- Anticorrosive and antirust paints must comply with Green Seal Standard GC-3.
- Clear wood finishes, floor coatings, stains, primers, and shellacs applied to interior elements must comply with South Coast Air Quality Management District (SCAQMD) Rule 1113.

Schools:

All paints and coatings used in the building interior must meet the testing and product requirements of the California Department of Health Services Standard Practice for the Testing of Volatile Organic Emissions from Various Sources Using Small-Scale Environmental Chambers, including 2004 Addenda.

IMPLEMENTATION

- Include VOC limits or identify specific products within the project specifications.
- For LEED for Schools projects, specify only those materials that meet the requirements of the referenced standard.

DOCUMENTATION & CALCULATIONS

Track all paints and coatings used in the project.

The VOC Budget Methodology compares the design case with a baseline case in order to demonstrate that the overall low-VOC performance has been attained. When the design is less than the baseline, the credit requirement is satisfied. If a product with higher than allowable VOC content is used, follow the VOC budget approach to determine whether the credit can still be achieved.

NOTES

The VOC threshold limits and content are generally expressed in grams per liter (g/L).

Schools projects may choose from IEQ Credits 4.1–4.6, Low-Emitting Materials, for a maximum of four points.

Per the USGBC Performance/Intent Equivalent Alternative Compliance Path (PIEACP) dated July 7, 2008, LEED for Schools projects may substitute the LEED for New Construction v2.2 credit requirements in place of the LEED for Schools requirements for this credit.

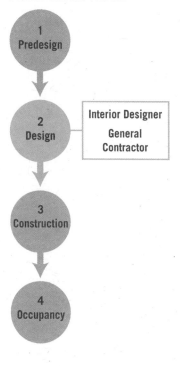

TIME LINE/TEAM

1 Predesign

2 Design — Interior Designer / General Contractor

3 Construction

4 Occupancy

STANDARDS

NC and CS:

Green Seal Standard GS-11, Paints, First Edition, May 20, 1993

Green Seal Standard GC-3, Anti-Corrosive Paints, Second Edition, January 7, 1997

South Coast Air Quality Management District (SCAQMD) Rule 1113, Architectural Coatings, effective January 1, 2004

Schools:

California Department of Health Services Standard Practice for the Testing of Volatile Organic Emissions from Various Sources Using Small-Scale Environmental Chambers, including 2004 Addenda

KEY TERMS

CONTAMINANTS

INDOOR AIR QUALITY (IAQ)

OCCUPANTS

VOLATILE ORGANIC COMPOUNDS

RELATED CREDITS

IEQ Prerequisite 2: Environmental Tobacco Smoke (ETS) Control

IEQ Prerequisite 3: Minimum Acoustical Performance (Schools only)

IEQ Credit 3.1: Construction IAQ Management Plan – During Construction

IEQ Credit 3.2: Construction IAQ Management Plan – Before Occupancy

IEQ Credit 4.1: Low-Emitting Materials – Adhesives and Sealants

IEQ Credit 4.2: Low-Emitting Materials – Paints and Coatings

IEQ Credit 4.4: Low-Emitting Materials – Composite Wood and Agrifiber Products

IEQ Credit 4.5: Low-Emitting Materials – Furniture and Furnishings (Schools only)

IEQ Credit 4.6: Low-Emitting Materials – Ceiling and Wall Systems (Schools only)

IEQ Credit 5: Indoor Chemical and Pollutant Source Control

IEQ Credit 9: Enhanced Acoustical Performance (Schools only)

INTENT

To reduce the quantity of indoor air contaminants that are odorous, irritating, and/or harmful to the comfort and well-being of installers and occupants.

REQUIREMENTS

NC and CS:

All flooring installed in the building interior must comply with the following conditions as applicable to the project scope:

- All carpet must meet The Carpet and Rug Institute Green Label Plus program requirements.
- All carpet cushion must meet The Carpet and Rug Institute Green Label program requirements.
- All carpet adhesive must meet the requirements of IEQ Credit 4.1, Low-Emitting Materials, Adhesives and Sealants (VOC limit of 50 g/L).
- All hard surface flooring must be certified as compliant with the FloorScore standard.
- Concrete, wood, bamboo, and cork floor finishes must meet the requirements of South Coast Air Quality Management District (SCAQMD) Rule 1113, Architectural Coatings.
- Tile setting adhesives and grout must meet SCAQMD Rule 1168, VOC Limits.

Schools:

All flooring products must meet the testing and product requirements of the California Department of Health Services Standard Practice for the Testing of Volatile Organic Emissions from Various Sources Using Small-Scale Environmental Chambers, including 2004 Addenda.

IMPLEMENTATION

- Include certification requirements and VOC limits and/or identify specific products within the project specifications.
- For LEED for Schools projects, specify only those materials that meet the requirements of the referenced standard.

DOCUMENTATION & CALCULATIONS

Track all carpet, carpet cushion, carpet adhesive, hard surface flooring, tile setting adhesive, finishes, and grout used in the project.

NOTES

Flooring products covered by FloorScore include vinyl, linoleum, laminate flooring, wood flooring, ceramic flooring, rubber flooring, and wall base.

The VOC threshold limits and content are generally expressed in grams per liter (g/L).

Schools projects may choose from IEQ Credits 4.1–4.6, Low-Emitting Materials, for a maximum of four points.

Per the USGBC Performance/Intent Equivalent Alternative Compliance Path (PIEACP) dated July 7, 2008, LEED for Schools projects may substitute the LEED for New Construction v2.2 credit requirements in place of the LEED for Schools requirements for this credit.

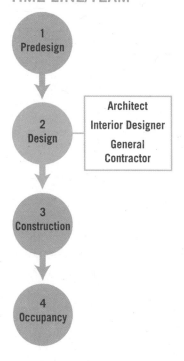

TIME LINE/TEAM

1 Predesign

2 Design — Architect / Interior Designer / General Contractor

3 Construction

4 Occupancy

STANDARDS

The Carpet and Rug Institute (CRI) Green Label Plus Testing Program

South Coast Air Quality Management District (SCAQMD) Rule 1168, VOC Limits

SCAQMD Rule 1113, Architectural Coatings

FloorScore™ Program

California Department of Health Services Standard Practice for the Testing of Volatile Organic Emissions from Various Sources Using Small-Scale Environmental Chambers, including 2004 Addenda

NC: 1 Point
Schools: 1 Point
CS: 1 Point

IEQ Credit 4.4: Low-Emitting Materials, Composite Wood and Agrifiber Products

KEY TERMS

AGRIFIBER PRODUCTS

COMPOSITE WOOD

CONTAMINANTS

FORMALDEHYDE

INDOOR AIR QUALITY (IAQ)

OFF-GASSING

UREA-FORMALDEHYDE

RELATED CREDITS

IEQ Prerequisite 2: Environmental Tobacco Smoke (ETS) Control

IEQ Prerequisite 3: Minimum Acoustical Performance (Schools only)

IEQ Credit 3.1: Construction IAQ Management Plan – During Construction

IEQ Credit 3.2: Construction IAQ Management Plan – Before Occupancy

IEQ Credit 4.1: Low-Emitting Materials – Adhesives and Sealants

IEQ Credit 4.2: Low-Emitting Materials – Paints and Coatings

IEQ Credit 4.3: Low-Emitting Materials – Flooring Systems

IEQ Credit 4.5: Low-Emitting Materials – Furniture and Furnishings (Schools only)

IEQ Credit 4.6: Low-Emitting Materials – Ceiling and Wall Systems (Schools only)

IEQ Credit 5: Indoor Chemical and Pollutant Source Control

IEQ Credit 9: Enhanced Acoustical Performance (Schools only)

INTENT

To reduce the quantity of indoor air contaminants that are odorous, irritating, and/or harmful to the comfort and well-being of installers and occupants.

REQUIREMENTS

NC and CS:

Composite wood and agrifiber products used in the interior of the building must contain no added urea-formaldehyde resins.

Laminate adhesives used to fabricate on-site and shop-applied composite wood and agrifiber assemblies must not contain added urea-formaldehyde resins.

Schools:

All composite wood and agrifiber products installed in the building interior must meet the testing and product requirements of the California Department of Health Services Standard Practice for the Testing of Volatile Organic Emissions from Various Sources Using Small-Scale Environmental Chambers, including 2004 Addenda.

IMPLEMENTATION

Include requirements or identify specific products within the project specifications.

For LEED for Schools projects, specify only those materials that meet the requirements of the referenced standard.

DOCUMENTATION & CALCULATIONS

Track all composite wood and agrifiber products installed in the project, and retain documentation confirming that they contain no added urea-formaldehyde resins.

For LEED for Schools projects, retain documentation confirming that the products meet the referenced standard.

NOTES

Composite wood and agrifiber products are defined as particleboard, medium-density fiberboard (MDF), plywood, wheatboard, strawboard, panel substrates, and door cores.

Schools projects may choose from IEQ Credits 4.1–4.6, Low-Emitting Materials, for a maximum of four points.

Per the USGBC Performance/Intent Equivalent Alternative Compliance Path (PIEACP) dated July 7, 2008, LEED for Schools projects may substitute the LEED for New Construction v2.2 credit requirements in place of the LEED for Schools requirements for this credit.

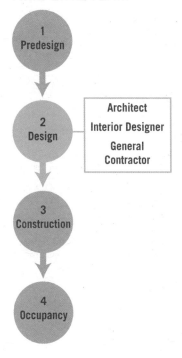

TIME LINE/TEAM

1 Predesign

2 Design — Architect / Interior Designer / General Contractor

3 Construction

4 Occupancy

STANDARDS

Schools:

California Department of Health Services Standard Practice for the Testing of Volatile Organic Emissions from Various Sources Using Small-Scale Environmental Chambers, including 2004 Addenda

NC and CS:

None

KEY TERMS

CONTAMINANTS

INDOOR AIR QUALITY (IAQ)

OCCUPANTS

OFF-GASSING

VOLATILE ORGANIC COMPOUNDS (VOCS)

RELATED CREDITS

IEQ Prerequisite 2: Environmental Tobacco Smoke (ETS) Control

IEQ Credit 3.1: Construction IAQ Management Plan – During Construction

IEQ Credit 3.2: Construction IAQ Management Plan – Before Occupancy

IEQ Credit 4.1: Low-Emitting Materials – Adhesives and Sealants

IEQ Credit 4.2: Low-Emitting Materials – Paints and Coatings

IEQ Credit 4.3: Low-Emitting Materials – Flooring Systems

IEQ Credit 4.4: Low-Emitting Materials – Composite Wood and Agrifiber Products

IEQ Credit 4.6: Low-Emitting Materials – Ceiling and Wall Systems (Schools only)

IEQ Credit 5: Indoor Chemical and Pollutant Source Control

INTENT

To reduce the quantity of indoor air contaminants that are odorous, irritating, and/or harmful to the comfort and well-being of installers and occupants.

REQUIREMENTS

All new classroom furniture must meet one of the following three options:

Option 1:
The furniture must be GREENGUARD Children and Schools certified.
Option 2:
Calculated indoor air concentrations must be less than or equal to those listed below, as determined by a procedure based on the EPA Environmental Technology Verification (ETV) Large Chamber Test Protocol for Measuring Emissions of VOCs and Aldehydes (September 1999) testing protocol conducted by an independent testing laboratory.
Option 3: (Schools)
Calculated indoor air concentrations must be less than or equal to those established below for furniture systems and seating, as determined by a procedure based on the ANSI/BIFMA M7.1–2007 and ANSI/BIFMA X7.1–2007 testing protocol conducted by an independent testing laboratory.

Table 1 from the LEED Reference Guide for Green Building Design and Construction, 2009. Page 501. Maximum Indoor Air Concentrations.

Chemical Contaminant	Classroom Furniture	Seating
Total VOCs	0.5 mg/m³	0.25 mg/m³
Formaldehyde	50 parts per billion	25 parts per billion
Total aldehydes	100 parts per billion	50 parts per billion
4—Phenylcyclohexene (4-PCH)	0.0065 mg/m³	0.00325 mg/m³

IMPLEMENTATION

Specify only those materials that meet the requirements of one of the referenced standards.

DOCUMENTATION & CALCULATIONS

Track all new furniture installed in the project and retain documentation to confirm that it meets one of the three eligibility criteria.

NOTES

Classroom furniture includes all student and teacher desks, tables, and seats that were manufactured, refurbished, or refinished within one year prior to occupancy.

Systems furniture may be either a panel-based workstation or a free-standing grouping of furniture items whose components have been designed to work in concert.

Seating covered by this credit is defined as task and guest chairs used with systems furniture.

Work tools attached to systems furniture are not included in the credit requirement.

Other furniture is considered occasional furniture and does not need to be included.

Salvaged and used furniture that is more than 1 year old at the time of occupancy is excluded from the credit.

Schools projects may choose from IEQ Credits 4.1–4.6, Low-Emitting Materials, for a maximum of four points.

TIME LINE/TEAM

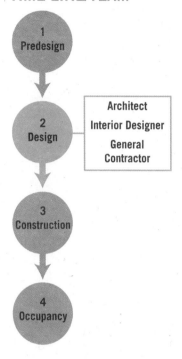

1 Predesign

2 Design — Architect / Interior Designer / General Contractor

3 Construction

4 Occupancy

STANDARDS

ANSI/BIFMA X7.1–2007, Standard for Formaldehyde and TVOC Emissions of Low-Emitting Office Furniture Systems and Seating

Environmental Technology Verification (ETV) Large Chamber Test Protocol for Measuring Emissions of VOCs and Aldehydes, effective September 1999, U.S. EPA

GREENGUARD Certification Program

KEY TERMS

AGRIFIBER BOARD

COMPOSITE WOOD

CONTAMINANTS

INDOOR AIR QUALITY (IAQ)

OCCUPANTS

OFF-GASSING

VOLATILE ORGANIC COMPOUNDS (VOCS)

RELATED CREDITS

 IEQ Prerequisite 2: Environmental Tobacco Smoke (ETS) Control

IEQ Credit 3.1: Construction IAQ Management Plan – During Construction

IEQ Credit 3.2: Construction IAQ Management Plan – Before Occupancy

IEQ Credit 4.1: Low-Emitting Materials – Adhesives and Sealants

 IEQ Credit 4.2: Low-Emitting Materials – Paints and Coatings

IEQ Credit 4.3: Low-Emitting Materials – Flooring Systems

 IEQ Credit 4.4: Low-Emitting Materials – Composite Wood and Agrifiber Products

IEQ Credit 4.5: Low-Emitting Materials – Furniture and Furnishings (Schools only)

IEQ Credit 5: Indoor Chemical and Pollutant Source Control

INTENT

To reduce the quantity of indoor air contaminants that are odorous, irritating, and/or harmful to the comfort and well-being of installers and occupants.

REQUIREMENTS

All gypsum board, insulation, acoustical ceiling systems, and wall coverings installed must meet the testing and product requirements of the California Department of Health Services Standard Practice for the Testing of Volatile Organic Emissions from Various Sources Using Small-Scale Environmental Chambers, including 2004 Addenda.

IMPLEMENTATION

Specify only those materials that meet the requirements of the referenced standard.

DOCUMENTATION & CALCULATIONS

Document that all ceiling and wall systems meet the referenced standard.

NOTES

Schools projects may choose from IEQ Credits 4.1–4.6, Low-Emitting Materials, for a maximum of four points.

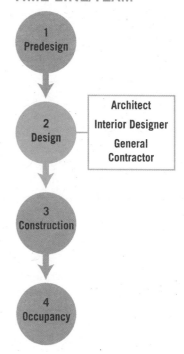

TIME LINE/TEAM

1 Predesign

2 Design

Architect
Interior Designer
General Contractor

3 Construction

4 Occupancy

STANDARDS

California Department of Health Services Standard Practice for the Testing of Volatile Organic Emissions from Various Sources Using Small-Scale Environmental Chambers, including 2004 Addenda

KEY TERMS

INDOOR AIR QUALITY (IAQ)

MINIMUM EFFICIENCY REPORTING VALUE (MERV)

REGULARLY OCCUPIED SPACES

RELATED CREDITS

IEQ Prerequisite 1: Minimum Indoor Air Quality Performance

IEQ Credit 1: Outdoor Air Delivery Monitoring

IEQ Credit 3.1: Construction IAQ Management Plan During Construction

IEQ Credit 3.2: Construction IAQ Management Plan – Before Occupancy

EA Prerequisite 1: Fundamental Commissioning

EA Prerequisite 2: Minimum Energy Performance

EA Credit 1: Optimize Energy Performance

EA Credit 3: Enhanced Commissioning

INTENT

To minimize building occupant exposure to potentially hazardous particulates and chemical pollutants.

REQUIREMENTS

- Use entryway systems, at least 10 feet long in the direction of travel, at all regularly used entrances.
- Exhaust all hazardous chemical storage and use areas.
- Install MERV 13 or higher filters in mechanical ventilation systems.
- Provide appropriate containment for appropriate disposal of hazardous liquid waste.

IMPLEMENTATION

- Incorporate permanent entryway systems at all high-traffic entrances.
- Locate and physically separate chemical storage areas (including areas with high-volume copy, print, and fax equipment) in enclosed rooms away from regularly occupied adjacent spaces, and equip these areas with a dedicated exhaust system.
- Design the mechanical system to accommodate MERV 13 filtration, and install new filters immediately prior to occupancy.
- In areas where chemical concentrate mixing occurs (such as housekeeping areas and science laboratories), install appropriate liquid waste containment.

DOCUMENTATION & CALCULATIONS

Identify the entryway systems on floor plans, and reference the individual entryway systems to a listing. Also, identify all rooms or areas where chemical use is anticipated.

NOTES

If roll-out mats are used in lieu of permanent entryway systems, contract with a service organization to maintain the mats on a weekly basis.

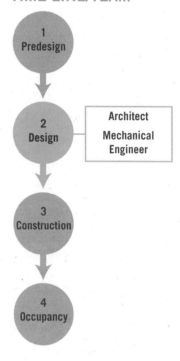

TIME LINE/TEAM

1 Predesign

2 Design — Architect / Mechanical Engineer

3 Construction

4 Occupancy

STANDARDS

ANSI/ASHRAE Standard 52.2–1999: Method of Testing General Ventilation Air-Cleaning Devices for Removal Efficiency by Particle Size

KEY TERMS

AUDIOVISUAL (A/V)

CORE LEARNING SPACES

CONTROLS

INDIVIDUAL OCCUPANT SPACES

NONOCCUPIED SPACE

GROUP MULTI-OCCUPANT SPACES

RELATED CREDITS

 IEQ Credit 6.2: Controllability of Systems – Thermal Comfort

 IEQ Credit 8: Daylight and Views

EA Prerequisite 1: Fundamental Commissioning

EA Prerequisite 2: Minimum Energy Performance

EA Credit 1: Optimize Energy Performance

EA Credit 3: Enhanced Commissioning

INTENT

To provide a high level of lighting system control by individual occupants or groups in multi-occupant spaces (such as classrooms and conference areas) and promote occupants' productivity, comfort, and well-being.

REQUIREMENTS

NC:
Install individual lighting controls for at least 90% of occupants and provide group lighting controls for all shared multi-occupant spaces.
Schools:
Install individual lighting controls for 90% of occupants within administrative and other nonclassroom areas. For learning spaces (including classrooms, gymnasiums, studios, and so on), provide group lighting controls. In classrooms, there must be at least two lighting modes for general illumination and A/V.

IMPLEMENTATION

Lighting controls in multi-occupant spaces must sufficiently permit adjustments to meet the needs and preferences of the occupants.

Ninety percent or more of the occupants located at work spaces intended for individual use must have task lighting.

Schools:

Classrooms must have a minimum of two lighting scenes, or presets. One must be configured for general use, and the other should accommodate a typical A/V presentation.

IEQ Credit 6.1: Controllability of Systems, Lighting (NC and Schools)

DOCUMENTATION & CALCULATIONS

Maintain a list of lighting controls by space type, confirming that all multi-occupant spaces have suitable controllability.

To determine how many individual lighting controls are necessary, multiply the number of workstations by 90%.

NOTES

Occupants who have control over their environment are more comfortable in a space.

TIME LINE/TEAM

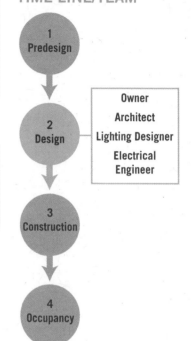

1 Predesign

2 Design

Owner
Architect
Lighting Designer
Electrical Engineer

3 Construction

4 Occupancy

STANDARDS

None

NC: 1 Point
Schools: 1 Point
CS: 1 Point

IEQ Credit 6.2: Controllability of Systems, Thermal Comfort (NC & Schools)
IEQ Credit 6: Controllability of Systems, Thermal Comfort (CS)

KEY TERMS

COMFORT CRITERIA

CONTROLS

HVAC SYSTEMS

INDIVIDUAL OCCUPANT SPACES

NATURAL VENTILATION

NONOCCUPIED SPACES

REGULARLY OCCUPIED SPACES

GROUP MULTI-OCCUPANT SPACES

THERMAL COMFORT

RELATED CREDITS

 IEQ Credit 5: Indoor Chemical and Pollutant Source Control

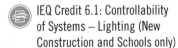 IEQ Credit 6.1: Controllability of Systems – Lighting (New Construction and Schools only)

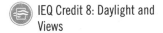 IEQ Credit 8: Daylight and Views

EA Prerequisite 1: Fundamental Commissioning

EA Prerequisite 2: Minimum Energy Performance

EA Credit 1: Optimize Energy Performance

EA Credit 3: Enhanced Commissioning

EA Credit 5: Measurement and Verification

INTENT

To provide a high level of thermal comfort system control by individual occupants or groups in multi-occupant spaces (such as classrooms or conference areas) and promote occupants' productivity, comfort, and well-being.

REQUIREMENTS

Install comfort controls for at least 50% of building occupants.

Provide comfort system controls for all shared multi-occupant spaces.

LEED Core & Shell projects that do not include thermal comfort systems cannot earn this credit.

IMPLEMENTATION

- Provide individuals and groups the ability to adjust their thermal environment within the space.

- Design the comfort systems so that 50% (or more) of individual workstations have thermal comfort controls. Confirm that all shared multi-occupant spaces have thermal comfort control.

IEQ Credit 6.2: Controllability of Systems, Thermal Comfort (NC & Schools)
IEQ Credit 6: Controllability of Systems, Thermal Comfort (CS)

Exemplary Performance

No

DOCUMENTATION & CALCULATIONS

Maintain a list of thermal comfort controls per space type.

To determine how many individual thermal comfort controls are necessary, multiply the number of workstations by 50%.

NOTES

Thermal comfort controllability is defined as control over one or more of the primary thermal comfort factors (air temperature, radiant temperature, air speed, or humidity).

Operable windows can be used instead of controls for workstations located 20 feet inside and no more than 10 feet to either side of the window if they meet the requirements of ASHRAE 62.1–2007, Paragraph 5.1, Natural Ventilation.

TIME LINE/TEAM

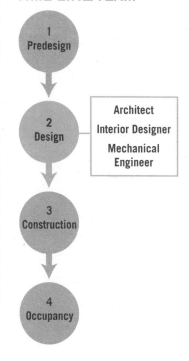

1 Predesign

2 Design — Architect / Interior Designer / Mechanical Engineer

3 Construction

4 Occupancy

STANDARDS

ASHRAE 62.1–2007: Ventilation for Acceptable Indoor Air Quality

ASHRAE 55–2004: Thermal Environmental Conditions for Human Occupancy

IEQ Credit 7.1: Thermal Comfort, Design (NC and Schools)
IEQ Credit 7: Thermal Comfort, Design (CS)

KEY TERMS

COMFORT CRITERIA

MECHANICAL VENTILATION

MIXED-MODE VENTILATION

NATURAL VENTILATION

OCCUPANTS

THERMAL COMFORT

RELATED CREDITS

IEQ Prerequisite 1: Minimum Indoor Air Quality Performance

IEQ Credit 2: Increased Ventilation

IEQ Credit 6.2: Controllability of Thermal Systems – Thermal Comfort

IEQ Credit 7.2: Thermal Comfort – Verification

EA Prerequisite 1: Fundamental Commissioning

EA Prerequisite 2: Minimum Energy Performance

EA Credit 1: Optimize Energy Performance

EA Credit 3: Enhanced Commissioning

EA Credit 5: Measurement and Verification

INTENT

To provide a comfortable thermal environment that promotes occupant productivity and well-being.

REQUIREMENTS

Design the HVAC system to comply with ASHRAE 55–2004.

Schools:
For natatoriums (swimming pool buildings), comply with "Typical Natatorium Design Conditions," defined in Chapter 4 of the ASHRAE HVAC Applications Handbook, 2003 Edition.
CS:
The base building mechanical systems must allow for the tenant build-out to comply with ASHRAE 55–2004. If the HVAC system is not included as part of the core and shell construction, this credit cannot be earned.

IMPLEMENTATION

The HVAC designer evaluates the anticipated occupant within the space and designs the heating, cooling, and ventilation strategies accordingly. The activity level and attire of the occupants directly affect how comfortable people are within a given environment. It is important for the designer to consider all six primary comfort factors when designing a comfortable building:

- Metabolic rate (activity level);
- Clothing insulation;
- Air temperature;
- Radiant temperature;
- Air speed; and
- Humidity.

IMPLEMENTATION, CONTINUED

Additional considerations include seasonal setpoint recommendations, change-over schedules, maintenance and operation instructions, and a maintenance and inspection schedule.

DOCUMENTATION & CALCULATIONS

The owner's project requirements and the mechanical engineer's basis of design should be reflected in design plans.

NOTES

None

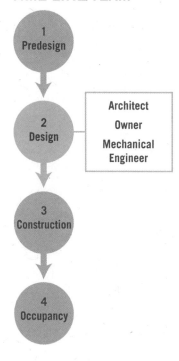

TIME LINE/TEAM

1 Predesign

2 Design — Architect / Owner / Mechanical Engineer

3 Construction

4 Occupancy

STANDARDS

ASHRAE 55–2004, Thermal Comfort Conditions for Human Occupancy

Chartered Institute of Building Services Engineers (CIBSE) Applications Manual 10–2005, Natural Ventilation in Non-Domestic Buildings

Schools: ASHRAE HVAC Applications Handbook, 2003 Edition, Chapter 4 (Places of Assembly), "Typical Natatorium Design Conditions"

IEQ Credit 7.2: Thermal Comfort, Verification (NC and Schools)

KEY TERMS

COMFORT CRITERIA

MECHANICAL VENTILATION

MIXED-MODE VENTILATION

NATURAL VENTILATION

OCCUPANTS

THERMAL COMFORT

RELATED CREDITS

 IEQ Prerequisite 1: Minimum IAQ Performance

 IEQ Credit 2: Increased Ventilation

IEQ Credit 6.2: Controllability of Thermal Systems – Thermal Comfort

IEQ Credit 7.1: Thermal Comfort – Design

EA Prerequisite 1: Fundamental Commissioning

EA Credit 3: Enhanced Commissioning

INTENT

To provide for the assessment of building occupants' thermal comfort over time.

REQUIREMENTS

Conduct an anonymous thermal comfort survey of building occupants within 6 to 18 months after the building has been occupied, and develop a plan for corrective action.

For new construction, also provide a permanent monitoring system to measure and record environmental variables.

Residential projects cannot earn this credit.

IMPLEMENTATION

● Create and administer a survey about thermal comfort conditions in person, over the phone, over networked computers, or on paper.

● Have in place a plan for corrective action.

● New Construction (additional requirement):
  ○ Install metering equipment to record environmental variables.

DOCUMENTATION & CALCULATIONS

Save a copy of the thermal comfort survey, and document the plan for corrective action.

NOTES

To be eligible for this credit, the LEED project must earn IEQ Credit 7.1, Thermal Comfort, Design.

TIME LINE/TEAM

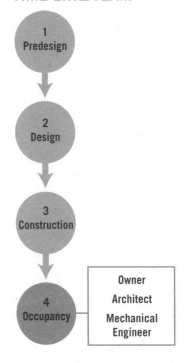

1 Predesign

2 Design

3 Construction

4 Occupancy

Owner
Architect
Mechanical Engineer

STANDARDS

ASHRAE 55–2004, Thermal Environmental Conditions for Human Occupancy

IEQ Credit 8.1: Daylight and Views, Daylight

KEY TERMS

FOOTCANDLE

VISIBLE LIGHT TRANSMITTANCE

REGULARLY OCCUPIED SPACE

VISION GLAZING

RELATED CREDITS

IEQ Credit 6: Controllability of Systems

IEQ Credit 8.2: Daylight and Views – Views

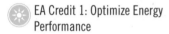
EA Prerequisite 2: Minimum Energy Performance

EA Credit 1: Optimize Energy Performance

INTENT

To provide building occupants with a connection between indoor spaces and the outdoors through the introduction of daylight and views into the regularly occupied areas of the building.

REQUIREMENTS

NC and CS:
Achieve daylight in 75% of regularly occupied spaces.
Schools:
Achieve daylight in 75% (one point) or 90% (two points) of classroom spaces.
If daylight is achieved for at least 75% of classroom spaces, the team can earn an additional point by daylighting 75% of the regularly occupied nonclassroom spaces.
NC, CS, and Schools:
Adequate daylight can be demonstrated by any of the following methods:

Option 1: Through computer simulation, show that the spaces are daylit between 25 and 500 footcandles.

Option 2: Use a prescriptive approach to determine the daylight zone. The calculation differs for side-lighting and top-lighting daylight zones.

Option 3: Take physical measurements to show that indoor daylight is at least 25 footcandles.

Option 4: Use a combination of the above options.

Exemplary Performance: NC, CS: 95%, Schools: 90% in classrooms, 95% in all other areas.

IMPLEMENTATION

Optimize building geometry and further enhance daylighting through strategic placement of windows, skylights, and light shelves.

Select glazing that will increase daylighting for occupants, and consider glare-control options for maximum controllability.

For daylighting, provide sunlight redirection and/or glare-control devices.

IMPLEMENTATION

The prescriptive daylighting strategies are often the hardest to understand.

For Side-Lighting Daylight Zone:

- The window-to-floor ratio multiplied by the visible light transmittance must be between 0.150 and 0.180 to qualify.

- Only window areas above 30 inches can count in the calculation.

- The ceiling obstruction rules sound complicated, but they're pretty simple: If a portion of the ceiling obstructs the entrance of daylight, the related floor area must be excluded from the compliant floor area.

For Top-Lighting Daylight Zone:

- The daylight zone under a skylight is the outline of the opening beneath the skylight plus, in each direction, the lesser of three options:
  - Seventy percent of the ceiling height;
  - One-half the distance to the edge of the nearest skylight (to prevent double counting of floor area from multiple skylights); or
  - The distance to any permanent opaque partition (such as a built-in bookshelf) farther away than 70% of the distance between the top of the partition and the ceiling.
- Roof skylights must cover between 3% and 6% of the roof area, the distance between the skylights must not be more than 1.4 times the ceiling height, and the glazing must have a minimum 0.5 VLT.

- If a skylight diffuser is used, it must have a measured haze value of greater than 90%.

TIME LINE/TEAM

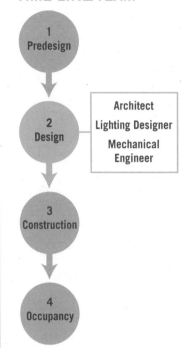

STANDARDS

ASTM D1003-07E1, Standard Test Method for Haze and Luminous Transmittance of Transparent Plastics

DOCUMENTATION & CALCULATIONS

Include floor plans, sections, and elevations showing daylighting strategies and the glare-control methods used in the project.

If using daylight simulation, update the computer model as the design progresses, and create a final report summarizing the simulation results.

NOTES

Glare control is required for daylighting to prevent discomfort or disability due to glare. It also helps regulate heat gain due to sunlight.

	NC: 1 Point Schools: 1 Point CS: 1 Point	IEQ Credit 8.2: Daylight and Views, Views

KEY TERMS

REGULARLY OCCUPIED SPACE

VISION GLAZING

RELATED CREDITS

 IEQ Credit 6: Controllability of Systems

 IEQ Credit 8.1: Daylight and Views – Daylight

EA Prerequisite 2: Minimum Energy Performance

EA Credit 1: Optimize Energy Performance

INTENT

To provide building occupants a connection to the outdoors through the introduction of daylight and views into the regularly occupied areas of the building.

REQUIREMENTS

Provide views to the exterior for 90% of all regularly occupied spaces.

IMPLEMENTATION

Locate open seating areas near the exterior to maximize views for all occupants. Provide glazing for core offices and multi-occupant spaces to enhance views.

A direct line of sight must exist through vision glazing between 30 and 90 inches above the floor.

Draw it out:

- Sketch a line of sight at 42 inches (typical seated eye height) across the section (looking at it from the side) to establish eye height and any obstruction to the perimeter glazing.

- In plan view (looking at it from the top), the area is within sight lines drawn from perimeter vision glazing.

- Double windows count too. The line of sight can be drawn through interior glazing as long as the occupant can see out another window.

- The compliant area depends on the space use type.

- Private offices: The entire square footage of the office is counted if more than 75% of the area has a direct line of sight.

- Multi-occupant spaces: Include only the actual square footage with a direct line of sight.

DOCUMENTATION & CALCULATIONS

- Show locations of regularly occupied spaces with views, and maintain a spreadsheet documenting the view area.

NOTES

Core & Shell projects must include a feasible tenant layout when determining whether interior spaces will maintain access to views.

TIME LINE/TEAM

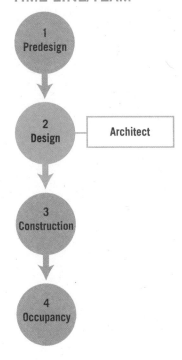

STANDARDS

None

KEY TERMS

BUILDING ENVELOPE

RELATIVE HUMIDITY

RELATED CREDITS

IEQ Credit 3.1: Construction IAQ Management Plan – During Construction

IEQ Credit 7.1: Thermal Comfort – Design

IEQ Credit 7.2: Thermal Comfort – Verification

INTENT

To reduce the potential presence of mold in schools through preventive design and construction measures.

REQUIREMENTS

Achieve IEQ Credit 3.1, Construction Indoor Air Quality Management Plan, During Construction; IEQ Credit 7.1, Thermal Comfort, Design; and IEQ Credit 7.2, Thermal Comfort, Verification.

Design the HVAC system to limit relative humidity to 60% or less at all times.

Develop an ongoing IAQ management program based on the EPA publication Building Air Quality: A Guide for Building Owners and Facility Managers.

Exemplary Performance: Yes, on a case-by-case basis.

IMPLEMENTATION

- Eliminate the potential for condensation.
- Pay special attention to known generators of condensation.
- Prevent mold during unoccupied periods.
- Address floods and leaky or failed equipment.
- Design for mold prevention.

DOCUMENTATION & CALCULATIONS

Document the ongoing IAQ management plan. Confirm how relative humidity is maintained under 60%. Confirm that the required credits are attained.

NOTES

None

TIME LINE/TEAM

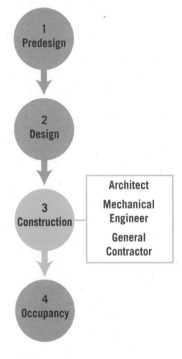

1 Predesign

2 Design

3 Construction — Architect / Mechanical Engineer / General Contractor

4 Occupancy

STANDARDS

Building Air Quality: A Guide for Building Owners and Facility Managers, U.S. Environmental Protection Agency, December 1991

1 List several ways to prevent mold growth.

_____

_____

2 What factors determine how comfortable people are within an indoor environment?

_____

_____

3 What are major sources of pollution in buildings, and what are some potential strategies to manage them?

_____

_____

4 What building features should design teams take into account when assessing daylight and views?

_____

_____

5 List items that will be addressed in an effective IAQ management plan during the construction phase:

_____

_____

IEQ LEARNING ACTIVITIES

Walk through an office or school building in your community and identify features that affect indoor environmental quality.

List the current state of each feature as effective, neutral, ineffective or absent.

FEATURE	EFFECTIVE	NEUTRAL	INEFFECTIVE	ABSENT
Daylighting				
Ventilation				
Operable windows				
Occupant control of lighting				
Occupant control of temperature				
Low-emissions materials				
High-efficiency air filters				
Green cleaning products and technologies				
Other				

WALK AROUND

1. Determine the MERV ratings of filters in the HVAC in your place of work.

2. Determine the VOC content of all cleaning products in your work building.

3. Determine whether you have lighting and/or thermal comfort control that meets the requirements of IEQ Credit 6, Controllability of Systems, in the space in which you work.

INVESTIGATE

Sketch the floor plan of your office, place of work, or other space where you spend time on a regular basis. Following the prescriptive option (Option 2) of IEQ Credit 8.1, Daylight and Views, Daylight, determine whether your working area meets the prescriptive requirements as a daylit space. Make reasonable assumptions to address any possible unknown values (such as the visible transmittance of windows, specific floor or window areas, and so on).

THINK ABOUT IT

IEQ PRACTICE QUESTIONS

1 When should indoor air quality testing be completed?

    a) Upon sealing the exterior envelope

    b) Before porous surfaces have been sealed

    c) During functional testing

    d) After all punch-list items have been completed

    e) Immediately following initial occupancy

2 IEQ Credit 9, Enhanced Acoustical Performance, addresses _____?

    a) Reverberation time and background noise.

    b) Sound transmission and background noise.

    c) Reverberation time and interior finishes.

    d) Sound transmission and interior finishes.

3 A project team is considering pursuit of IEQ Credit 2, Increased Ventilation. Which factors should be considered to determine whether this credit is appropriate for the project? (Select two.)

    a) Estimated impact on energy use

    b) Added first cost for extra controls

    c) Improved air quality for occupants

    d) Effect on thermal comfort controls

4 A LEED for New Construction project team that is pursuing IEQ Credit 4.1, Low-Emitting Materials, Adhesives and Sealants, discovers that a subcontractor has inadvertently used a small quantity of noncompliant contact adhesive. The product has a VOC content of 85 grams per liter, but the credit threshold is 80 grams per liter. How should the team proceed?

    a) Forgo pursuit of IEQ Credit 4.1.

    b) Complete a VOC budget calculation.

    c) Submit a Credit Interpretation Request.

    d) Conduct a precompletion building flush-out.

5 A LEED for New Construction project decides it will prohibit smoking in the building. What else must be done to meet the requirements of IEQ Prerequisite 2, Environmental Tobacco Smoke (ETS) Control? (Select two.)

    a) Prohibit smoking within 25 feet of building openings.

    b) Provide dedicated smoking areas.

    c) Prohibit smoking within 10 feet of pedestrian thoroughfares.

    d) Provide signage to restrict smoking activity.

    e) Enforce smoking restrictions.

See Answer Key on page 220.

INNOVATION IN DESIGN

The Innovation in Design (ID) category recognizes projects for exceptional performance in established LEED credits and for innovative green building features that fall outside of the LEED rating system.

REGIONAL PRIORITY

The Regional Priority (RP) category addresses regionally unique environmental issues and encourages design teams to focus on issues that are particularly important for their project site.

WHAT ABOUT INNOVATION AND REGIONAL PRIORITY?

- How would you demonstrate the environmental benefit of an innovative design strategy?

- If you were asked to write a new credit for LEED, what would it be?

- What are the most pressing concerns about new development in your community?

- How can a building help to transform a community?

INNOVATION IN DESIGN & REGIONAL PRIORITY

ID CREDIT 1: Innovation in Design

Evaluate products based on ISO 14040 life-cycle assessment

Provide an electronic equipment recycling program for community members

Provide an educational program on environmental and human health benefits of green building

RP CREDIT 1: Regional Priority

Exemplary Performance

ID CREDIT 2: LEED® Accredited Professional (AP)

LEED AP

THE OVERVIEW

If you like to go above and beyond to achieve ever greater environmental benefits for your project, then you've come to the right place! This category provides project teams with the opportunity to be awarded points for the following:

- Exceptional performance in the established requirements in existing LEED credits;
- Innovative performance in green building topics not specifically addressed by LEED;
- Primary project team member participation as a LEED Accredited Professional;
- (Schools only) Integration of the sustainable school facility features with the school's educational mission; and
- (Regional Priority) Achievement of credits that address environmental issues unique to a region.

As a general rule of thumb, ID credits for exceptional performance are awarded for doubling the credit requirements and/or achieving the next incremental percentage threshold. For instance, an ID credit for exemplary performance in WE Credit 3, Water Use Reduction, would require a minimum

of 45% savings. The logic is that two points are awarded at 30% savings, a third point is awarded at 35%, and a fourth point is awarded at 40%, so the next logical increment is 45%.

ID credits for innovative performance are awarded for strategies that demonstrate quantifiable environmental benefits. Strategies for sustainable building design and construction are constantly evolving and improving, and new technologies that improve building performance are continually introduced to the marketplace. Examples of innovative performance ID credits are the following:

- Educational Outreach Program;
- Green Housekeeping;
- High Volume Fly Ash;
- ISO 14040 Life-Cycle Assessment;
- Waste Management and Diversion Programs;
- Low-Emitting Furniture and Furnishings; and
- Organic Landscaping/Integrated Pest Management Program.

The ID credit for LEED Accredited Professional exists to support and encourage the design integration on a project team. This person should serve a primary function in the application and certification process. Similarly, by designing a curriculum based on the high-performance features of the school building in a LEED for Schools project, you will heighten student awareness of environmental issues and understanding of the integrated design, construction, and operations process.

Additionally, the strategies explored in the LEED for New Construction, Core & Shell, and Schools Rating Systems have different environmental significance across the country and even within a city. Each distinct environmental region has been allocated six credits that address its specific prioritized environmental issues. A project that earns a Regional Priority credit automatically earns one point in addition to any points awarded for that credit. Up to four extra points can be earned in this way, with only one point earned per credit.

SYNERGIES

The credits in this category require an integrated design process that addresses every category in LEED for New Construction, Core & Shell, and Schools. For ideas and strategies for ID opportunities, refer to the "Exemplary Performance" section of each credit in the reference guide and/or the "Exemplary Performance Matrix" in the appendix of this study guide. For a list of applicable RP credits, visit the Regional Priority database at www.usgbc.org.

INNOVATION IN DESIGN & REGIONAL PRIORITY

CATEGORY HIGHLIGHTS

- New Construction and Core & Shell: Teams can earn ID points in three ways: demonstrate exemplary performance in existing LEED credits, apply innovations not covered elsewhere in LEED, and have a LEED Accredited Professional on the project team.

- Schools: An additional type of ID credit is available for schools only (ID Credit 3, The School As a Teaching Tool); nonetheless, projects can still earn only a maximum of six points for the category, because Schools projects can only achieve up to four points for ID Credit 1, Innovation in Design.

- You have to prove your case in order to succeed! The project team must write its own credit by following the format and rigor established in the LEED rating system and prove that it has met the requirements of its new credit.

- You must be able to demonstrate significant and measurable environmental benefit.

- LEED ID credits are evaluated for each project. It is important to note that the awarding of an ID credit for one project at a specific point in time does not constitute automatic approval for a similar strategy in a future project.

INNOVATION IN DESIGN & REGIONAL PRIORITY

CREDIT	TITLE	NC	SCHOOLS	CS
ID Credit 1	Innovation in Design	1-5 points	1-4 points	1-5 points
ID Credit 2	LEED® Accredited Professional	1 point	1 point	1 point
ID Credit 3	The School as a Teaching Tool	N/A	1 point	N/A

CREDIT	TITLE	NC	SCHOOLS	CS
RP Credit 1	Regional Priority	1-4 points	1-4 points	1-4 points

KEY TERMS

LEED Accredited Professional (AP)	An individual who has successfully completed the LEED professional accreditation exam. Accreditation certifies that the individual has the knowledge and skills necessary to participate in the LEED application and certification process, holds a firm understanding of green building practices and principles, and is familiar with LEED requirements, resources, and processes.
Regional Priority	USGBC's regional councils, chapters, and affiliates have identified the environmental concerns that are locally most important for every region of the country. Six LEED credits that address those local priorities were selected for each region. A project that earns a Regional Priority credit will earn one bonus point in addition to any points awarded for that credit. Up to four extra points can be earned in this way.

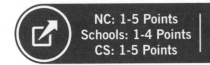
ID Credit 1:
Innovation in Design

KEY TERMS

None

RELATED CREDITS

None

INTENT

To provide design teams and projects the opportunity to achieve exceptional performance above the requirements set by the LEED Green Building Rating System and/or innovative performance in green building categories not specifically addressed by the LEED Green Building Rating System.

REQUIREMENTS

Credits can be achieved through any combination of the paths below.

Achieve significant, measurable environmental performance using a strategy not already addressed in the LEED 2009 for New Construction, Core & Shell, or Schools Rating Systems.

Path 1: Innovation in Design (one to five points for NC and CS; one to four points for Schools)

Identify the following in writing:

- The intent of the proposed innovation credit;
- The proposed requirements for compliance;
- The proposed submittals to demonstrate compliance; and
- The design approach (strategies) used to meet the requirement.

Path 2: Exemplary Performance (one to three points)

Achieve exemplary performance in an existing prerequisite or credit that allows exemplary performance. An exemplary performance point may be earned for achieving double the credit requirements and/or achieving the next incremental percentage threshold of an existing credit in LEED.

IMPLEMENTATION

- **Path 1:** Innovative strategies are those that are not addressed by any existing LEED credits. Three basic criteria must be met:
    - The credit must demonstrate quantitative performance improvements for environmental benefit.
    - The process or specification must be comprehensive.
    - The concept the project team develops for the innovation credit must be applicable to other projects and must be significantly better than standard sustainable design practices.

IMPLEMENTATION, CONTINUED

- **Path 2:** Double the credit requirements and/or achieve the next incremental percentage threshold.

DOCUMENTATION & CALCULATIONS

- Document the process by which the project team has worked to develop and/or implement additional environmental benefits.

- Be prepared to make your case by explaining the new proposed credit (Path 1) with the same rigor as an established LEED credit.

- Track your development and implementation process to illustrate the specific exceptional and innovative strategies used.

NOTES

- Keep thinking! New environmental building and design opportunities are continually emerging.

TIME LINE/TEAM

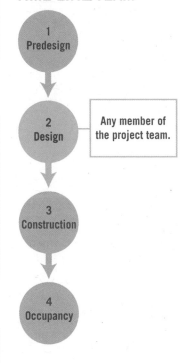

Any member of the project team.

STANDARDS

None

NC: 1 Point	ID Credit 2:
Schools: 1 Point	**LEED® Accredited Professional (AP)**
CS: 1 Point	

KEY TERMS

LEED ACCREDITED PROFESSIONAL
(AP)

RELATED CREDITS

None

INTENT

To support and encourage the design integration required by LEED to streamline the application and certification process.

REQUIREMENTS

At least one key project team member needs to be a LEED AP.

IMPLEMENTATION

Two options:

- Engage an individual within the organization who is already a LEED AP to participate in the application and certification process.

- Hire an experienced LEED AP.

DOCUMENTATION & CALCULATIONS

Obtain confirmation from team members who are LEED APs.

NOTES

LEED APs understand what is required to design a LEED space and how to coordinate the documentation process for LEED certification.

TIME LINE/TEAM

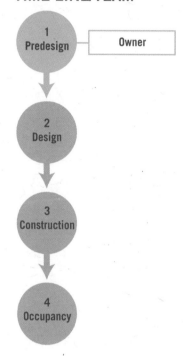

STANDARDS

LEED Accredited Professional (AP)

Green Building Certification Institute (GBCI), www.gbci.org

KEY TERMS

None

RELATED CREDITS

None

INTENT

To integrate the sustainable features of a school facility with the school's educational mission.

REQUIREMENTS

Design a curriculum based on the high-performance features of the building, and commit to implementing the curriculum within 10 months of LEED certification. The curriculum must meet local or state curriculum standards, be approved by school administrators, and provide 10 or more hours of classroom instruction per year per full-time student.

IMPLEMENTATION

- Use the physical school environment as an educational interface.

- Integrate hands-on learning exercises to enhance the educational experience and allow students to interact with the everyday functions of their facility.

ID Credit 3:
The School As a Teaching Tool (Schools)

Exemplary Performance

DOCUMENTATION & CALCULATIONS

- School administrators should work with the project team to develop the curriculum.

- Prove that the curriculum has been reviewed and approved by school administrators and meets applicable local and state curriculum standards.

NOTES

Think of all the LEED credits you have mastered and how you could integrate their implementation strategies and environmental benefits into a curriculum for a classroom!

TIME LINE/TEAM

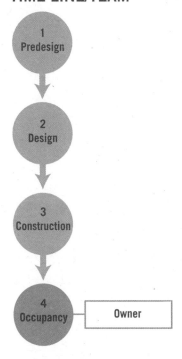

STANDARDS

LEED Accredited Professional (AP)

Green Building Certification Institute (GBCI), www.gbci.org

Innovation in Design   **211**

KEY TERMS

REGIONAL PRIORITY

RELATED CREDITS

None

INTENT

To provide an incentive for the achievement of credits that address geographically specific environmental priorities.

REQUIREMENTS

Earn one to four of the six Regional Priority credits identified by the USGBC regional councils and chapters as having environmental importance for a project's region. A database of Regional Priority credits and their geographic applicability is available on the USGBC website, www.usgbc.org.

One point is awarded for each Regional Priority credit achieved; no more than four credits identified as Regional Priority credits may be earned. Projects outside the United States are not eligible.

IMPLEMENTATION

Refer to the "Implementation" section under a particular Regional Priority credit.

RP Credit 1:
Regional Priority

Exemplary Performance No

DOCUMENTATION & CALCULATIONS

Refer to the "Documentation Guidance" and "Calculations" sections under each Regional Priority credit in the reference guide.

NOTES

None

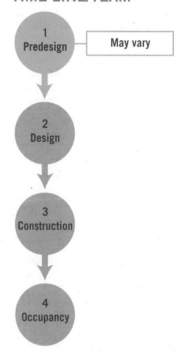

TIME LINE/TEAM

1 Predesign — May vary

2 Design

3 Construction

4 Occupancy

STANDARDS

Refer to the standards for a particular Regional Priority credit.

ID & RP CATEGORY REVIEW

1 How many credits can you think of that are eligible for exemplary performance? What are the requirements for achieving exemplary performance for these credits?

_____

_____

2 What strategies must you implement to achieve an Innovation in Design credit for a Green Educational Program?

_____

_____

3 What are some of the primary benefits of having a LEED AP on your project team?

_____

_____

4 List unique environmental issues by region and note how they could be applied to credits within LEED for New Construction, Core & Shell, and Schools.

_____

_____

ID & RP LEARNING ACTIVITIES

List the exemplary performance credits you think are most easily achievable and note why. Which ones do you think are most difficult?

CREDIT	REQUIREMENT

Now, write your own **LEED** credit based on an idea you have about a possible sustainable operations innovation.

CREDIT	REQUIREMENT

THINK ABOUT IT

Talk to three people and discuss pressing regional issues for green building and development in your community. Relate them back to the **LEED** credits.

ASK AROUND

Investigate a couple of **LEED** projects in your area or in the **USGBC** case studies and see which **ID** points were earned.

INVESTIGATE

1 A project team is interested in pursuing bonus credit under the Regional Priority section. How can the team identify the credits that have been assigned additional weighting for the project's region?

a) Submit a Credit Interpretation Request.

b) Consult the local USGBC chapter.

c) Refer to the USGBC website.

2 A LEED for Schools project is pursuing ID Credit 3, The School As a Teaching Tool. The design team has created a detailed project narrative to support the use of the building as a teaching tool. What must the curriculum developers do to satisfy the credit requirements?

a) Review the project narrative, modify it to be grade-level appropriate, and distribute it to all students.

b) Develop coursework based on the building that explores the connection to ecological principles.

c) Engage student learning by hosting a design charrette.

d) Provide the narrative to teaching staff and ask that they incorporate elements of it into existing lesson plans.

3 As a rule of thumb, Innovation in Design credits for exemplary performance are awarded for _____. (Select two.)

a) Reaching a 100% threshold.

b) Doubling the credit requirements.

c) Achieving the next incremental threshold.

d) Demonstrating significant environmental benefit.

4 Which of the following would disqualify a strategy from earning ID Credit 1, Innovation in Design, as an innovative strategy? (Select two.)

a) The strategy is not cost-effective.

b) The approach addresses only part of the LEED project.

c) The environmental benefit cannot be quantified.

d) The concept requires ongoing analysis and/or maintenance.

e) The strategy aids in the achievement of another LEED credit.

f) The methodology is applicable only to certain geographic locations.

5 A project team has multiple LEED APs serving on the project, including the design architect, urban ecologist, and lighting designer. How does this support the design integration required by LEED?

a) LEED AP status is required to access LEED Online.

b) The LEED AP completes the LEED Submittal Templates.

c) The LEED AP has a demonstrated understanding of the LEED rating systems.

d) The LEED AP can answer Credit Interpretation Requests from the project team.

See Answer Key on page 220.

PRACTICE QUESTION ANSWER KEY

SUSTAINABLE SITES PRACTICE QUESTION ANSWERS

1. **B, D.** Proximity to basic services is recognized under SS Credit 2, Development Density and Community Connectivity, and proximity to mass transit is recognized under SS Credit 4.1, Alternative Transportation, Public Transportation Access. Proximity to local organic farms and bicycle paths is not recognized within LEED for Core & Shell.

2. **C.** Option 3 of this credit allows a combination of approaches in achieving the credit, which is solved for this project as follows: (Area of Roof Meeting Minimum SRI / 0.75) + (Area of Vegetated Roof / 0.5) ≥ Total Roof Area.

The SRI of the roof is 69, which meets the SRI requirement for steep-sloped roof areas but not low-sloped roof areas. Therefore, 6,000 square feet (60% of the total roof area) is compliant roof area. Plugging this into the equation:

(6,000 sf / 0.75) + (Area of Vegetated Roof / 0.5) ≥ 10,000 sf

Further reducing the equation:

8,000 sf + (Area of Vegetated Roof / 0.5) ≥ 10,000 sf

Further reducing the equation:

Area of Vegetated Roof / 0.5 ≥ 2,000 sf

Solving the equation:

Area of Vegetated Roof ≥ 1,000 sf

There is 2,000 square feet of flat roof area (20% of 10,000 sf), and, of this area, 1,000 square feet must be vegetated. So 50% (1,000 sf / 2,000 sf) of the flat roof area must be vegetated to comply with the credit requirements.

3. **B.** If the ASTM Phase I assessment concludes that environmental contamination is likely to be present at the site, it is required that an ASTM Phase II assessment be completed. If the Phase II assessment concludes that contamination is present, the site must be remediated to comply with the prerequisite, while also earning SS Credit 3, Brownfield Redevelopment.

4. **D.** Residential projects must provide covered bicycle parking for 15% of building occupants. Showers are not required for residential occupants, as they are assumed to have access to showering facilities within their dwelling units.

5. **C.** Light trespass is defined as a component of light pollution that is emitted horizontally onto adjacent properties (as contrasted with sky glow, which is light pollution emitted upward). Fixture shielding, while potentially contributing to sky glow control, is primarily meant to address light trespass.

WATER EFFICIENCY PRACTICE QUESTION ANSWERS

1. **D.** Lavatories for public use have a baseline flow rate of 0.5 gallons per minute. This flow rate is established by the Universal Plumbing Code (UPC) and International Plumbing Code (IPC) and goes beyond the EPAct of 1992 baseline requirements.

2. **A, C, E.** The intent of WE Credit 2, Innovative Wastewater Technologies, is to reduce wastewater generation and potable water demand while increasing local aquifer recharge.

3. **D.** Wastewater from toilets and urinals is always considered blackwater.

4. **B, D.** Increasing irrigation efficiency and designing the site landscaping for a low landscape coefficient are acceptable methods of reducing the landscape water use per the LEED calculation methodology. The landscaped area must remain the same in both the baseline and the design calculations, and the use of groundwater is considered equivalent to the use of potable water for the purposes of this credit.

5. **A, D.** All LEED for Schools projects pursing this credit must ensure that refrigeration equipment does not use once-through cooling with potable water. Additionally, garbage disposals are prohibited for projects pursuing this credit.

ENERGY AND ATMOSPHERE PRACTICE QUESTION ANSWERS

1. **B, C.** Decreasing the lighting power density reduces heat gain in the space, thereby reducing the need to offset these gains with mechanical cooling. Additionally, increasing the building mass can allow the space to maintain cooler temperatures during the day and warmer temperatures at night, further reducing the need for mechanical conditioning.

2. **A.** The International Performance Measurement and Verification Protocol (IPMVP) Volume III: Concepts and Options for Determining Energy Savings in New Construction has been established by EVO and is the referenced standard for EA Credit 5, Measurement and Verification.

3. **B, D.** Only certain biofuels are recognized as eligible to qualify as renewable energy. Animal waste and landfill gas are allowable, while municipal solid waste is not. Additionally, while clean wood is permitted, wood contaminated with paints, halogens, arsenic, and other chemicals is not allowed. Finally, geo-exchange systems (geothermal or ground-source heat pumps) are earth-coupled HVAC applications that use vapor compression for heat transfer. These systems do not obtain significant quantities of deep-earth heat compared with geothermal electric systems and are ineligible as a renewable energy system.

4. **C.** Once the owner's project requirements (OPR) are documented, the design team develops its basis of design (BOD) documentation to form the foundation for the commissioning process. The submittal review and design review(s) are to be conducted against the OPR and BOD to ensure that the design intent is maintained. The

functional testing takes place once the systems are installed and operational, and the systems manual is delivered after completion of functional testing.

5. **B.** The tenant M&V plan is intended as a resource for tenants to advise them on how to integrate into the building monitoring system.

MATERIALS & RESOURCES PRACTICE QUESTION ANSWERS

1. **B, C, E.** The door can contribute toward MR Credit 4, Recycled Content, due to its preconsumer recycled content; toward MR Credit 7, Certified Wood, due to its FSC certification; and toward MR Credit 5, Regional Materials, because its harvest, processing, and manufacture took place within 500 miles of the project site.

2. **C.** The credit requirements define rapidly renewable as materials that are typically harvested within a 10-year or shorter cycle.

3. **A, D, E.** Structural floors, framing, and slabs are all eligible components for a building to be considered under MR Credit 1.1, Building Reuse, Maintain Existing Walls, Floors, and Roof. Window assemblies are specifically excluded, as are any hazardous materials.

4. **B.** Of the 100 tons of waste, 20 tons are soils that are excluded from consideration under this credit, for a total eligible waste of 80 tons. The 20 tons that were landfilled, as well as the 20 tons that were incinerated (regardless of their use for energy generation), are considered nondiverted. Therefore, 40 tons of the 80 tons were diverted, for a final diversion rate of 50%.

5. **D.** This prerequisite requires collection and storage of paper, corrugated cardboard, glass, plastic, and metal. While it is advisable to collect all recyclable materials, only these five are specifically required by LEED.

INDOOR ENVIRONMENTAL QUALITY PRACTICE QUESTION ANSWERS

1. **D.** IAQ testing must be completed after construction is complete and before occupancy. Once punch lists have been finished, construction is complete.

2. **B.** This credit addresses sound transmission and background noise beyond those levels required by IEQ Prerequisite 3, Minimum Acoustical Performance.

3. **A, C.** Energy use is directly affected by the amount of outside air that is delivered to the space. Energy is generally required to move the air through the building (fan energy) as well as to maintain comfortable temperatures and humidity (HVAC energy). Increased ventilation is known to reduce the concentration of air contaminants to improve air quality for occupants. The need for increased ventilation should be balanced with the need to reduce overall energy use.

4. **B.** A VOC budget calculation is allowable for projects that intentionally or unintentionally use products that exceed the established threshold for the specific application. Since the quantity applied is small, and the VOC levels are only slightly exceeded, it is likely that the VOC budget calculation will yield compliant results.

5. **A, D.** Smoking must be prohibited within 25 feet of all building entrances, operable windows, and air intakes. Additionally, signage must be posted to allow smoking in designated areas, prohibit smoking in designated areas, or prohibit smoking on the entire property.

INNOVATION IN DESIGN & REGIONAL PRIORITY PRACTICE QUESTION ANSWERS

1. **C.** Regional Priority credits are listed on the USGBC website.

2. **B.** This Innovation in Design credit requires that curriculum be developed based on the high-performance features of the building and relating to human ecology and natural ecology. A minimum of 10 hours of classroom instruction per year per student must be delivered.

3. **B, C.** Exemplary performance credits are awarded for exceeding the threshold, in a significant way, of existing LEED credits. The established thresholds for each credit's exemplary performance are listed in the reference guide, although the general rule is that the levels are either doubled or in line with a consistent progression.

4. **B, C.** Innovative Strategy credits must be comprehensive in nature (addressing an issue across the LEED project), applicable to other projects, significantly better than standard sustainable design practices, and quantifiable.

5. **C.** LEED AP status is not required to complete the LEED Submittal Templates or to access LEED Online. Additionally, only USGBC can answer Credit Interpretation Requests. The LEED AP, in passing the professional accreditation exam, has demonstrated a level of understanding of USGBC and LEED, and therefore serves as a valuable resource to project teams pursuing LEED certification.

ACRONYMS AND ORGANIZATIONS

ANSI	American National Standards Institute
AP	LEED Accredited Professional
APPA	Association of Physical Plant Administrators
ASHRAE	American Society of Heating, Refrigerating and Air-Conditioning Engineers
CFC	Chlorofluorocarbon
cfm	cubic feet per minute
CIR	Credit Interpretation Request
COC	Chain of Custody
CRI	The Carpet and Rug Institute
DHW	Domestic hot water
DOE	U.S. Department of Energy
EA	Energy and Atmosphere category
EER	Energy Efficiency Rating
EPA	U.S. Environmental Protection Agency
ET	Evapotranspiration
FSC	Forest Stewardship Council
GHGs	Greenhouse Gases
gpf	gallons per flush
gpm	gallons per minute
GS	Green Seal
HCFC	Hydrochlorofluorocarbon
HEPA	Eigh-Efficiency Particle Absorbing
HVAC	Heating, Ventilation and Air Conditioning
Hz	Hertz
IAP	ENERGY STAR with Indoor Air Package
IAQ	indoor air quality
IEQ	Indoor Environmental Quality category
IESNA	Illuminating Engineering Society of North America
IPC	International Plumbing Code
kW	kilowatt

kWh	kilowatt-hour
LED	Light-Emitting Diode
LEED	Leadership in Energy and Environmental Design
MERV	Minimum Efficiency Reporting Value
MR	Materials and Resources category
SEER	Seasonal Energy Efficiency Rating
SHGC	Solar Heat Gain Coefficient
SMACNA	Sheet Metal and Air Conditioning Contractors' National Association
SRI	Solar Reflectance Index
SS	Sustainable Sites category
UPC	Uniform Plumbing Code
USGBC	U.S. Green Building Council
VOC	Volatile Organic Compound
WE	Water Efficiency category

CREDIT REVIEW SHEET

Test your knowledge of individual credits. Make several printed copies of this sheet, then fill in the blanks from memory for each credit you want to practice.

CATEGORY: _____ NUMBER: _____ AVAILABLE POINTS: _____

NAME: _____

EXEMPLARY PERFORMANCE: _____

TIME LINE: _____ TEAM: _____

INTENT:

_____

_____

REQUIREMENTS:

_____

_____

IMPLEMENTATION STRATEGIES:

_____

_____

REFERENCED STANDARDS:

_____

_____

RELATED CREDITS:

_____

_____

DOCUMENTATION & CALCULATIONS:

_____

_____

EQUATIONS:

_____

_____

ADDITIONAL NOTES:

_____

_____

KEY TERMS:

_____

_____

EXEMPLARY PERFORMANCE MATRIX

Exemplary performance strategies may be the result of performance that greatly exceeds the performance level that is required in an existing LEED for New Construction, Schools, or Core & Shell credit. To earn exemplary performance credits, teams must meet the performance level defined by the next step in the threshold progression.

SUSTAINABLE SITES		
CREDIT	**EXEMPLARY PERFORMANCE ELIGIBILITY**	**THRESHOLD**
SS Credit 2: Development Density and Community Connectivity	Projects must first meet the requirements of Option 1 under SS Credit 2, Development Density and Community Connectivity. Additionally, the project must meet one of the two following requirements: The project itself must have a density at least double that of the average density within the calculated area (see Equations 1 and 3); OR The average density within an area twice as large as that for the base credit achievement must be at least 120,000 square feet per acre. To double the area, use Equation 2, but double the project site area first.	Double calculated area density.
SS Credit 4: Alternative Transportation	For Option 1, project teams can earn one additional point by instituting a comprehensive transportation management plan that demonstrates a quantifiable reduction in personal automobile use through any of multiple alternative options. For Option 2, project teams can earn one additional point for double transit ridership if: The project is located within 1/2 mile of at least two existing commuter rail, light rail, or subway lines; OR The project is located within 1/4 mile of at least two stops for four or more public or campus bus lines usable by building occupants; AND Frequency of service must be at least 200 transit rides per day, total, at these stops.	Option 1, Comprehensive transportation management plan. Option 2, Double transit ridership.
SS Credit 6: Stormwater Design	By documenting a comprehensive approach to capturing and treating stormwater runoff and demonstrating performance above and beyond the credit requirements, project teams can earn one exemplary performance credit.	No standardized exemplary performance option has been established for this credit.
SS Credit 7.1: Heat Island Effect, Nonroof	Either (1) 100% of nonroof impervious surfaces have been constructed with high-albedo or open-grid paving, or will be shaded within five years; or (2) 100% of the on-site parking spaces have been located under cover.	100%
SS Credit 7.2: Heat Island Effect, Roof	A total of 100% of the project's roof area (excluding any mechanical equipment, photovoltaic panels, and skylights) consists of a vegetated roof system.	100%
SS Credit 10: Joint Use of Facilities (Schools only)	If two of the three options are met, projects may earn an Innovation in Design credit.	Meet 2 out of 3 options.

WATER EFFICIENCY

CREDIT	EXEMPLARY PERFORMANCE ELIGIBILITY	THRESHOLD
WE Credit 2: Innovative Wastewater Technologies	Either (1) by demonstrating 100% reduction in potable water use for sewage conveyance; or (2) by demonstrating on-site treatment and either reuse or infiltration of 100% of generated wastewater.	100%
WE Credit 3: Water Use Reduction	A total of 45% reduction in projected potable water use.	45%
WE Credit 4: Process Water Use Reduction (Schools only)	A total of 40% projected process water savings.	40%

ENERGY AND ATMOSPHERE

CREDIT	EXEMPLARY PERFORMANCE ELIGIBILITY	THRESHOLD
EA Credit 1: Optimize Energy Performance	For projects pursuing Option 1, Whole Building Simulation, that demonstrate a percentage improvement in the proposed building performance rating compared with the baseline building performance rating per ASHRAE 90.1–2007.	New buildings: 50% Existing building renovations: 46%
EA Credit 2: On-site Renewable Energy	NC and Schools: On-site renewable energy accounts for 15% or more of the annual building energy cost. CS: On-site renewable energy accounts for 5% or more of the annual building energy cost.	NC and Schools: 15% CS: 5%
EA Credit 3: Enhanced Commissioning	NC, CS, and Schools: Projects that conduct comprehensive envelope commissioning may consider an innovation credit if they demonstrate the standards and protocol by which the envelope was commissioned. CS: Projects that require the full scope of commissioning (both fundamental and enhanced) for all the tenant spaces may be considered for an innovation point.	Demonstrate the standards & protocol for envelope commissioning. Tenant space enhanced commissioning.
EA Credit 6: Green Power	A total of 100% electricity from renewable sources.	100%

MATERIALS AND RESOURCES

CREDIT	EXEMPLARY PERFORMANCE ELIGIBILITY	THRESHOLD
MR Credit 1: Building Reuse: Maintain Existing Walls, Floors, and Roof (Core & Shell only)	Maintain 95% or more of the existing walls, floors, and roof.	95%
MR Credit 2: Construction Waste Management	Divert 95% or more of total construction waste.	95%
MR Credit 3: Materials Reuse	NC and Schools: Salvaged or reused materials used on the project are 15% or more of the total materials cost. CS: Salvaged or reused materials used on the project are equal to at least 10% of the total materials cost.	NC and Schools: 15% CS: 10%
MR Credit 4: Recycled Content	Recycled-content value of 30% or more.	30%
MR Credit 5: Regional Materials	The total value of regionally harvested, extracted, and manufactured materials of 30% or more.	30%

MR Credit 6: Rapidly Renewable Materials (New Construction and Schools only)	A total of 5% or more of rapidly renewable materials.	5%
MR Credit 7: Certified Wood (Core & Shell, MR Credit 6)	A total of 95% or more of the project's total new wood value is FSC certified.	95%

INDOOR ENVIRONMENTAL QUALITY		
CREDIT	**EXEMPLARY PERFORMANCE ELIGIBILITY**	**THRESHOLD**
IEQ Credit 3: Construction Indoor Air Quality Management Plan (Core & Shell only)	Projects that require and enforce a construction indoor air quality management plan for 100% of tenant spaces.	100%
IEQ Credit 8: Daylight and Views	NC and CS: A total of 95% daylighting. Schools: A total of 90% of all classrooms and 95% daylighting in all other regularly occupied nonclassroom spaces.	NC and CS: 95% Schools: 90% daylight in classrooms and 95% daylight in nonclassroom spaces
IEQ Credit 9: Enhanced Acoustical Performance (Schools only)	If the project achieves an outdoor background noise level of 55 dBA for playgrounds and 60 dBA for athletic fields and all other school grounds, or an indoor noise level of 35 dBA.	55 dBA for playgrounds; 60 dBA for athletic fields; 35 dBA for indoors
IEQ Credit 10: Mold Prevention (Schools only)	Projects are evaluated on a case-by-case basis.	No prescribed threshold

REFERENCE STANDARD TABLE

REFERENCE TITLE	REFERENCE DESCRIPTION	WEBSITE
U.S. Green Building Council, Leadership in Energy and Environmental Design	The Leadership in Energy and Environmental Design (LEED) Green Building Rating System is a voluntary, consensus-based national rating system for developing high-performance, sustainable buildings. LEED addresses all building types and emphasizes state-of-the-art strategies in five subject areas: sustainable site development, water savings, energy efficiency, materials and resources selection, and indoor environmental quality.	www.usgbc.org
2003 EPA Construction General Permit	The construction general permit outlines a set of provisions construction operators must follow to comply with NPDES stormwater regulations. The permit covers any site 1 acre or larger as well as smaller sites that belong to a larger common plan of development or sale. It replaces and updates previous EPA permits.	http://cfpub. epa.gov/npdes/ stormwater/cgp. cfm
ASTM E1527–05, Phase I Environmental Site Assessment	A Phase I environmental site assessment is a report prepared for a real estate holding that identifies potential or existing environmental contamination liabilities. The analysis typically addresses both the underlying land as well as physical improvements to the property; however, a Phase I assessment does not involve actual collection of physical samples or chemical analyses of any kind. It includes consideration of potential soil contamination, groundwater quality, and surface water quality and sometimes considers issues related to hazardous substance uptake by biota. The examination of a site may include these actions: definition of any chemical residues within structures; identification of possible asbestos in building materials; inventory of hazardous substances stored or used on-site; assessment of mold and mildew; and evaluation of other indoor air quality parameters.	http://www.astm. org
ASTM E1903-97, Phase II Environmental Site Assessment, effective 2002	A Phase II environmental site assessment is an investigation that collects original samples of soil, groundwater, or building materials to analyze for quantitative values of various contaminants. This investigation is normally undertaken when a Phase I assessment has determined a potential for site contamination. The substances most frequently tested are petroleum hydrocarbons, heavy metals, pesticides, solvents, asbestos, and mold.	http://www.astm. org
U.S. Department of Agriculture, United States Code of Federal Regulations, Title 7, Volume 6, Parts 400 to 699, Section 657.5 (citation 7CFR657.5), Definition of Prime Agricultural Land	This standard states, "Prime farmland is land that has the best combination of physical and chemical characteristics for producing food, feed, forage, fiber, and oilseed crops and is also available for these uses (the land could be cropland, pastureland, rangeland, forest land, or other land, but not urban built-up land or water). It has the soil quality, growing season, and moisture supply needed to economically produce sustained high yields of crops when treated and managed, including water management, according to acceptable farming methods. In general, prime farmlands have an adequate and dependable water supply from precipitation or irrigation, a favorable temperature and growing season, acceptable acidity or alkalinity, acceptable salt and sodium content, and few or no rocks. They are permeable to water and air. Prime farmlands are not excessively erodible or saturated with water for a long period of time, and they either do not flood frequently or are protected from flooding. Examples of soils that qualify as prime farmland are Palouse silt loam, 0% to 7% slopes; Brookston silty clay loam, drained; and Tama silty clay loam, 0% to 5% slopes."	http://www. gpoaccess.gov/ cfr/index.html Go to "Browse and/or search the CFR." See also "Identification of Important Farmlands." ftp://ftp-fc. sc.egov.usda.gov/ CT/soils/2007_ prime-important. pdf
Federal Emergency Management Agency, Definition of 100-Year Flood	This referenced standard addresses flood elevations. FEMA defines a 100-year flood as the flood elevation that has a 1% chance of being reached or exceeded each year. It is not the most significant flood in a 100-year period. Instead, 100-year floods can occur many times within a 100-year period. See the FEMA website for comprehensive information on floods.	www.fema.gov

REFERENCE TITLE	REFERENCE DESCRIPTION	WEBSITE
Endangered Species Lists, U.S. Fish and Wildlife Service, List of Threatened and Endangered Species	This referenced standard addresses threatened and endangered wildlife and plants. The service also maintains a list of the country's native plants and animals that are candidates for addition to the federal list.	http://www.fws.gov/endangered/
National Marine Fisheries Service, List of Endangered Marine Species	In addition to this federal list, state agencies provide state-specific lists of endangered or threatened wildlife and plant species.	http://www.nmfs.noaa.gov/pr/species/esa_species.htm
United States Code of Federal Regulations, 40 CFR, Parts 230-233, and Part 22, Definition of Wetlands	This referenced standard addresses wetlands and discharges of dredged or filled material into waters regulated by states. The definition of wetland areas pertaining to this credit, found in Part 230, is as follows: "Wetlands consist of areas that are inundated or saturated by surface or ground water at a frequency and duration sufficient to support, and that under normal circumstances do support, a prevalence of vegetation typically adapted for life in saturated soil conditions."	http://www.gpoaccess.gov/cfr/index.html
U.S. EPA, Definition of Brownfields	With certain legal exclusions and additions, "brownfield site" means real property, the expansion, redevelopment, or reuse of which may be complicated by the presence or potential presence of a hazardous substance, pollutant, or contaminant (Public Law 107-118, H.R. 2869, Small Business Liability Relief and Brownfields Revitalization Act). See the website for additional information and resources.	www.epa.gov/brownfields
Institute of Transportation Engineers, Parking Generation Study, 2003	Parking Generation, third edition, represents a significant change from the 1987 edition. Three times as much data are now available, and 91 land uses are represented. In addition, this update incorporates parking demand data by hour of day. For the benefit of future analysis and research, this edition separates parking data records by various factors that may affect parking demand. The study links parking data to the hour of observation to provide a temporal understanding of parking demand and its peak hour. Additionally, this update separates out the influences of area type on parking demand, including (where data are available) information about sites that have priced parking.	http://www.ite.org
ASTM E408–71(1996)e1, Standard Test Methods for Total Normal Emittance of Surfaces Using Inspection-Meter Techniques	This standard describes how to measure total normal emittance of surfaces using a portable inspection-meter instrument. The test methods are intended for large surfaces where nondestructive testing is required. See the standard for testing steps and a discussion of thermal emittance theory.	http://www.astm.org
ASTM C1371–04a, Standard Test Method for Determination of Emittance of Materials Near Room Temperature Using Portable Emissometers	This test method covers a technique for determination of the emittance of typical materials using a portable differential thermopile emissometer. The purpose of the test method is to provide a comparative means of quantifying the emittance of opaque, highly thermally conductive materials near room temperature as a parameter in evaluating temperatures, heat flows, and derived thermal resistances of materials.	http://www.astm.org
ASTM E903–96, Standard Test Method for Solar Absorptance, Reflectance, and Transmittance of Materials Using Integrating Spheres	Referenced in the ENERGY STAR® roofing standard, this test method uses spectrophotometers and need only be applied for initial reflectance measurement. It specifies methods of computing solar-weighted properties using the measured spectral values. This test method is applicable to materials having both specular and diffuse optical properties. Except for transmitting sheet materials that are heterogeneous, patterned, or corrugated, this test method is preferred over Test Method E1084. The ENERGY STAR roofing standard also allows the use of reflectometers to measure roofing materials' solar reflectance.	http://www.astm.org

ASTM E1918–97, Standard Test Method for Measuring Solar Reflectance of Horizontal and Low-Sloped Surfaces in the Field	This test method covers the solar reflectance measurements, using a pyranometer, of various horizontal and low-sloped surfaces and materials. The test method is intended for use when the angle from a surface to the sun is less than 45 degrees.	http://www.astm.org
ASTM C1549–04, Standard Test Method for Determination of Solar Reflectance Near Ambient Temperature Using a Portable Solar Reflectometer	This test method covers a technique for determining the solar reflectance of flat, opaque materials in a laboratory or in the field using a commercial, portable solar reflectometer. The purpose of the test method is to provide the solar reflectance data required to evaluate temperature and heat flows across surfaces exposed to solar radiation.	http://www.astm.org
ANSI/ASHRAE/IESNA Standard 90.1–2007, Energy Standard for Buildings Except Low-Rise Residential Lighting, Section 9 (without amendments) American Society of Heating,	Refrigerating and Air-Conditioning Engineers Standard 90.1–2007 was developed by the American Society of Heating, Refrigerating and Air-Conditioning Engineers (ASHRAE) under an American National Standards Institute (ANSI) consensus process. The Illuminating Engineering Society of North America (IESNA) is a joint sponsor of the standard. Standard 90.1 establishes minimum requirements for the energy-efficient design of buildings, except those that are low-rise residential. The provisions of this standard also do not apply to single-family houses; multifamily structures of three habitable stories or fewer above grade; mobile and modular homes; buildings without electricity or fossil fuel consumption; or equipment and portions of building systems that use energy primarily for industrial, manufacturing, or commercial processes. The standard provides criteria in the following general categories: building envelope (Section 5); heating, ventilating, and air conditioning (Section 6); service water heating (Section 7); power (Section 8); lighting (Section 9); and other equipment (Section 10). Within each section there are mandatory provisions as well as additional prescriptive requirements. Some sections also contain a performance alternate. The energy cost budget option (Section 11) allows the user to exceed some of the prescriptive requirements provided energy cost savings are made in other prescribed areas. However, in all cases, the mandatory provisions must still be met. Section 9 of the standard provides requirements for the lighting of buildings. Only the exterior lighting requirements apply to this credit.	http://www.ashrae.org
The Energy Policy Act (EPAct) of 1992 (and as amended)	This U.S. act addresses energy and water use in commercial, institutional, and residential facilities.	
The Energy Policy Act (EPAct) of 2005	This statute became U.S. law in August 2005.	
International Association of Plumbing and Mechanical Officials Publication IAPMO/ American National Standards Institute UPC 1–2006, Uniform Plumbing Code 2006, Section 402.0, Water-Conserving Fixtures and Fittings	UPC defines water-conserving fixtures and fittings for water closets, urinals, and metered faucets. This ANSI-accredited code safeguards life, health, property, and public welfare by regulating and controlling the design, construction, installation, materials, location, operation, and maintenance or use of plumbing systems.	http://www.iapmo.org

REFERENCE TITLE	REFERENCE DESCRIPTION	WEBSITE
International Code Council, International Plumbing Code 2006, Section 604, Design of Building Water Distribution System	IPC defines maximum flow rates and consumption for plumbing fixtures and fittings, including public and private lavatories, showerheads, sink faucets, urinals, and water closets.	http://www. iccsafe.org
ANSI/ASHRAE/IESNA Standard 90.1–2007: Energy Standard for Buildings Except Low-Rise Residential	ANSI/ASHRAE/IESNA Standard 90.1–2007 was formulated by ASHRAE under an ANSI consensus process. IESNA is a joint sponsor of the standard. ANSI/ASHRAE/IESNA Standard 90.1–2007 establishes minimum requirements for the energy-efficient design of buildings, with these exceptions: single-family houses; multifamily structures of three habitable stories or fewer above grade; manufactured houses (mobile and modular homes); buildings that do not use either electricity or fossil fuel; and equipment and portions of building systems that use energy primarily for industrial, manufacturing, or commercial processes. Building envelope requirements are provided for semiheated spaces, such as warehouses.	http://www. ashrae.org
ASHRAE Advanced Energy Design Guide for Small Office Buildings 2004	The Advanced Energy Design Guide series provides a sensible approach to achieving advanced levels of energy savings without having to resort to detailed calculations or analysis. This guide is for office buildings up to 20,000 square feet; such buildings make up the bulk of office space in the United States. The strategies provide benefits and savings for the building owner while maintaining the quality and functionality of the office space.	http://www. ashrae.org
ASHRAE Advanced Energy Design Guide for Small Warehouses and Self Storage Buildings 2008	The Advanced Energy Design Guide series provides a sensible and easy approach to achieving advanced levels of energy savings without having to resort to detailed calculations or analysis. This guide focuses on warehouses up to 50,000 square feet and self-storage buildings that use unitary heating and air-conditioning equipment; such facilities make up a significant amount of commercial warehouse space in the United States.	http://www. ashrae.org
New Building Institute	The Advanced Energy Design Guide series provides a sensible and easy approach to achieving advanced levels of energy savings without having to resort to detailed calculations or analysis. This guide focuses on elementary, middle, and high school buildings, which have a wide variety of heating and air-conditioning requirements.	http://www. ashrae.org
New Building Institute, Advanced Building™ Core Performance™ Guide	The Advanced Building program provides a prescriptive plan for exceeding the energy performance requirements of ASHRAE 90.1–2004. The program was designed to provide a predictable alternative to energy performance modeling and a simple set of criteria for increasing building energy performance significantly. The Advanced Building Core Performance program updates and replaces the Advanced Building Benchmarked program. Core Performance is calibrated to exceed the requirements of ASHRAE 90.1–2004 in all climate zones. Information about the Core Performance program requirements and a range of additional reference material is available at http://www. advancedbuildings.net.	http://www. energystar. gov/index. cfm?c=new_ bldg_design. bus_target_finder
ENERGY STAR® Program, Target Finder Rating Tool	ENERGY STAR is a government–industry partnership managed by the U.S. Environmental Protection Agency and the U.S. Department of Energy. Target Finder is an online tool that can establish energy performance goals for a project. It uses data such as ZIP code and building type to calculate the estimated total energy use for the building,	

REFERENCE TITLE	REFERENCE DESCRIPTION	WEBSITE
	and then it assigns an energy performance rating on a scale of 1 to 100. The ZIP code is used to determine the climate conditions that the building would experience in a normal year (based on a 30-year climate average) and to estimate energy use intensity for the target based on the energy fuel mix typical in the region. The tool displays the percentage electricity and natural gas assumption used to calculate design targets. The energy use intensity generated by Target Finder reflects the distribution of energy performance in commercial buildings derived from data in the U.S. Department of Energy's Commercial Buildings Energy Consumption Survey. The ratings generated by Target Finder provide a useful benchmark for estimating and comparing a building's energy use with that of other buildings and for determining a project's goals for energy efficiency. Assessing energy consumption early in the process enables teams to employ a holistic approach in making design decisions that improve the building's performance. Energy performance targets are more easily achieved if all the building's systems enhance one another; attempting to increase energy efficiency after construction is less successful because only small changes are possible without major disruption and additional cost.	http://www. energystar. gov/index. cfm?c=new_ bldg_design. bus_target_finder
U.S. EPA Clean Air Act, Title VI, Section 608, Compliance with the Section 608 Refrigerant Recycling Rule	Under Section 608 of the Clean Air Act, the EPA has established regulations on using and recycling ozone-depleting compounds. An overview of the pertinent regulations and information about compliance can be found on this website.	http://www. epa.gov/ozone/ title6/608/ 608fact.html
ASHRAE Advanced Energy Design Guide for Retail Buildings 2006	The Advanced Energy Design Guide series provides a sensible and easy approach to achieving advanced levels of energy savings without having to resort to detailed calculations or analysis. This guide focuses on retail buildings up to 20,000 square feet that use unitary heating and air-conditioning equipment; such buildings represent a significant amount of commercial retail space in the United States.	http://www. ashrae.org
ASHRAE Advanced Energy Design Guide for K–12 School Buildings	The Advanced Energy Design Guide series provides a sensible and easy approach to achieving advanced levels of energy savings without having to resort to detailed calculations or analysis. This guide focuses on elementary, middle, and high school buildings, which have a wide variety of heating and air-conditioning requirements. Options for daylighting, an important component in schools, are included.	http://www. ashrae.org
International Performance Measurement and Verification Protocol, Volume III, EVO 30000.1–2006, Concepts and Options for Determining Energy Savings in New Construction, effective January 2006	The Efficiency Valuation Organization is a nonprofit organization whose vision is a global marketplace that properly values energy and water efficiency. IPMVP, Volume III, provides a concise description of best practice techniques for verifying the energy performance of new construction projects. Chapter 2 describes the process for developing the theoretical baseline for new construction projects and provides examples of relevant applications. Chapter 3 describes the basic concepts and structure of the measurement and verification plan. Chapter 4 describes specific measurement and verification methods for energy conservation measure isolation (Option B) and whole-building calibrated simulation (Option D). Volume III pertains to new construction projects; Volume I relates to retrofit projects in existing facilities.	http://www.evo-world.org

REFERENCE TITLE	REFERENCE DESCRIPTION	WEBSITE
Center for Resource Solutions, Green-e Product Certification Requirements	Green-e Energy is a voluntary certification and verification program for renewable energy products. Green-e certifies products that meet environmental and consumer protection standards developed in conjunction with environmental, energy, and policy organizations. Sellers of Green-e–certified energy must disclose clear and useful information to customers. Three types of renewable energy options are eligible for Green-e certification: renewable energy certificates, utility green-pricing programs, and competitive electricity products. The Green-e standard that went into effect on January 1, 2007, supersedes previous regional and product-specific criteria. Products exhibiting the Green-e logo are greener and cleaner than the average retail electricity product sold in that particular region. To be eligible for the Green-e logo, companies must meet certain criteria. The first criterion is the inclusion of qualified sources of renewable energy content, such as solar electric, wind, geothermal, biomass, and small or certified low-impact hydro facilities. Other criteria are the inclusion of new renewable energy content (to support new generation capacity); compliance with emissions regulations for the nonrenewable portion of the energy product; and the absence of nuclear power. Companies must also meet other criteria regarding renewable portfolio standards. Criteria are often specific to a state or region of the United States.	http://www. green-e.org
International Standard ISO 14021–1999, Environmental Labels and Declarations— Self-Declared Environmental Claims (Type II Environmental Labeling) International Organization for Standardization (ISO)	This international standard specifies requirements for self-declared environmental claims, including statements, symbols, and graphics, for products. It further describes selected terms commonly used in environmental claims and gives qualifications for their use. It also describes a general evaluation and verification methodology for self-declared environmental claims and specific evaluation and verification methods for the selected claims.	http://www.iso. org
Forest Stewardship Council Principles and Criteria	Certification by the Forest Stewardship Council (FSC) is a seal of approval awarded to forest managers who adopt environmentally and socially responsible forest management practices and to companies that manufacture and sell products made from certified wood. This seal enables consumers, including architects and specifiers, to identify and procure wood products from well-managed sources and thereby use their purchasing power to influence and reward improved forest management activities around the world. LEED accepts certification according to the comprehensive system established by the internationally recognized Forest Stewardship Council. FSC was created in 1993 to establish international forest management standards, known as the FSC principles and criteria, to ensure that forestry practices are environmentally responsible, socially beneficial, and economically viable. These principles and criteria are also intended to ensure the long-term health and productivity of forests for timber production, wildlife habitat, clean air and water supplies, climate stabilization, spiritual renewal, and social benefit. These global principles and criteria are translated into meaningful standards at a local level through region-specific standard-setting processes. FSC also accredits and monitors certification organizations. The certifiers are independent, third-party auditors that are qualified to annually evaluate compliance with FSC standards on the ground and to award certifications. There are two types of certification:	http://www.fscus. org

REFERENCE TITLE	REFERENCE DESCRIPTION	WEBSITE
	Forest management certification is awarded to responsible forest managers after their operations successfully complete audits of forestry practices and plans. **Chain-of-custody (COC) certification** is awarded to companies that process, manufacture, and/or sell products made of certified wood and that successfully complete audits to ensure proper use of the FSC name and logo; segregate certified and noncertified materials in manufacturing and distribution systems; and observe other relevant FSC rules (for example, meeting minimum requirements for FSC fiber content in assembled and composite wood products). The majority of FSC certification audits performed in North America are conducted by SmartWood and Scientific Certification Systems (SCS), which are based in the United States. A limited number are performed by SGS, which is based in Europe.	
American National Standards Institute (ANSI)/American Society of Heating, Refrigerating and Air-Conditioning Engineers (ASHRAE) Standard 62.1–2007: Ventilation for Acceptable Indoor Air Quality	This standard specifies minimum ventilation rates and IAQ levels so as to reduce the potential for adverse health effects. The standard specifies that ventilation systems be designed to prevent uptake of contaminants, minimize growth and dissemination of microorganisms, and, if necessary, filter particulates. The standard outlines a ventilation rate procedure and an IAQ procedure for compliance. The ventilation rate procedure prescribes outdoor air quality levels acceptable for ventilation; treatment measures for contaminated outdoor air; and ventilation rates for residential, commercial, institutional, vehicular, and industrial spaces. The IAQ procedure is a performance-based design approach in which the building and its ventilation system maintain concentrations of specific contaminants at or below certain determined limits to achieve an indoor air quality acceptable to building occupants and/or visitors. For the purposes of this procedure, acceptable perceived indoor air quality means there is no dissatisfaction related to thermal comfort, noise and vibration, lighting, and psychological stressors. The IAQ procedure also includes criteria for the following situations: reducing outdoor air quantities when recirculated air is treated by contaminant-removal equipment, and ventilating when a space's air volume is used as a reservoir to dilute contaminants. The IAQ procedure incorporates quantitative and subjective evaluation and restricts contaminant concentrations to acceptable levels. ASHRAE updated the standard in 2007 to include requirements for buildings that allow smoking in designated areas to separate areas with environmental tobacco smoke (ETS) from those without ETS. The standard now also clarifies how designers must analyze mechanical cooling systems to limit indoor relative humidity that would cause dampness-related problems such as mold and microbial growth.	http://www.ashrae.org
American National Standards Institute (ANSI)/ASTME–779–03, Standard Test Method for Determining Air Leakage Rate by Fan Pressurization	This test method covers a standardized technique for measuring air leakage rates through a building envelope under controlled pressurization and depressurization; it should produce a measurement of the air tightness of a building envelope.	http://www.astm.org

REFERENCE TITLE	REFERENCE DESCRIPTION	WEBSITE
Residential Manual for Compliance with California's 2001 Energy Efficiency Standards (For Low Rise Residential Buildings), Chapter 4	According to this chapter of the manual, "The Standards require quality design and construction of mechanical ventilation systems and air distribution systems. They also offer compliance credit for the construction of less leaky building envelopes. With the 2001 Standards, testing of ducts, refrigerant charge, and airflow [were] added to the prescriptive requirements (Package D) and [are] assumed as part of the standard design in performance calculations. Many of the compliance credit options require installer diagnostic testing and certification, and independent diagnostic testing and field verification by a certified home energy rater."	www.energy. ca.gov/ title24/archive /2001 standards/ residential_ manual/res_ manual_c hapter4.PDF
Sheet Metal and Air Conditioning Contractors National Association (SMACNA) IAQ Guidelines for Occupied Buildings under Construction, Second Edition, Chapter 3, November 2007	The Sheet Metal and Air Conditioning Contractors National Association (SMACNA) is an international organization that developed guidelines for maintaining healthful indoor air quality during demolitions, renovations, and construction. The full document covers air pollutant sources, control measures, IAQ process management, quality control and documentation, interpersonal communication, sample projects, tables, references, resources, and checklists.	http://www. smacna.org
American National Standards Institute (ANSI)/ASHRAE Standard 52.2–1999: Method of Testing General Ventilation Air-Cleaning Devices for Removal Efficiency by Particle Size	This standard presents methods for testing air cleaners for two performance characteristics: the device's capacity for removing particles from the air stream and the device's resistance to airflow. The minimum efficiency reporting value (MERV) is based on three composite average particle size removal efficiency points. Consult the standard for a complete explanation of MERV calculations.	http://www. ashrae.org
U.S. Environmental Protection Agency Compendium of Methods for the Determination of Air Pollutants in Indoor Air	This standard is available from NTIS, (800) 553-6847, with the ordering number PB90200288. According to the compendium, the EPA created this document to "provide regional, state and local environmental regulatory agencies with step-by-step sampling and analysis procedures for the determination of selected pollutants in indoor air. Determination of pollutants in indoor air is a complex task, primarily because of the wide variety of compounds of interest and the lack of standardized sampling and analysis procedures. The Compendium has been prepared to provide a standardized format for such analytical procedures. A core set of 10 chapters with each chapter containing [one] or more methods [is] presented in the current document. [The] Compendium covers a variety of active and passive sampling procedures, as well as several analytical techniques both on and off site..."	N/A; phone (800) 553-6847
South Coast Air Quality Management District (SCAQMD) Amendment to South Coast Rule 1168, VOC Limits, effective January 7, 2005	The South Coast Air Quality Management District is a governmental organization in Southern California with the mission to maintain healthful air quality for its residents. The organization established source-specific standards to reduce air quality impacts. Adhesives, sealants, and sealant primers must comply with SCAQMD Rule 1168. VOC limits listed in the corresponding table correspond to an effective date of July 1, 2005, and a rule amendment date of January 7, 2005.	http://www.aqmd. gov/rules/reg/ reg11/r1168.pdf
Green Seal Standard 36 (GS–36), effective October 19, 2000	Green Seal is an independent, nonprofit organization that strives to achieve a healthier and cleaner environment by identifying and promoting products and services that cause less toxic pollution and waste, conserve resources and habitats, and minimize global warming and ozone depletion. GS–36 sets VOC limits for commercial adhesives. Green Seal Standard for Commercial Adhesives GS–36 requirements went into effect on October 19, 2000.	http://www. greenseal.org/ certification/ standards/ commercial_ adhesives_ GS_36.cfm

REFERENCE TITLE	REFERENCE DESCRIPTION	WEBSITE
Green Seal Standard GS–11	Green Seal is an independent, nonprofit organization that strives to achieve a healthier and cleaner environment by identifying and promoting products and services that cause less toxic pollution and waste, conserve resources and habitats, and minimize global warming and ozone depletion. GS–11 sets VOC limits for commercial flat and nonflat paints. Tables 1 and 2 summarize Green Seal Standard GS–11.	http://www. greenseal.org/ certification/ standards/paints_ and_coatings.pdf
Green Seal Standard GC–3	GC–3 sets VOC limits for anticorrosive and antirust paints.	http://www. greenseal.org/ certification/ standards/anti- corrosivepaints. pdf
South Coast Air Quality Management District (SCAQMD) Rule 1113, Architectural Coatings	The South Coast Air Quality Management District is a governmental organization in Southern California with the mission to maintain healthful air quality for its residents. The organization established source-specific standards to reduce air quality impacts.	http://www.aqmd. gov/rules/reg/ reg11/r1113.pdf
The Carpet and Rug Institute (CRI) Green Label Plus Testing Program	The Carpet and Rug Institute (CRI) is a trade organization representing the carpet and rug industry. Green Label Plus is an independent testing program that identifies carpets with very low VOC emissions. The CRI website describes the program and the associated VOC emission criteria in micrograms per square meter per hour. These criteria were developed by The Carpet and Rug Institute (CRI) in coordination with California's Sustainable Building Task Force and the California Department of Health Services (DHS). In the CRI Green Label Plus Program, emission rates must be verified by annual tests. Approved certification numbers can be reviewed on the CRI website under "Indoor Air Quality/Green Label Plus/ Approved Companies." Approved products are listed under the company heading.	http://www. carpet-rug.com
South Coast Air Quality Management District (SCAQMD) Rule 1113, Architectural Coatings	The South Coast Air Quality Management District is a governmental organization in Southern California with the mission to maintain healthful air quality for its residents. The organization established source-specific standards to reduce air quality impacts.	http://www.aqmd. gov/rules/reg/ reg11/r1113.pdf
FloorScore™ Program	According to its website, "The FloorScore program, developed by the Resilient Floor Covering Institute (RFCI) in conjunction with Scientific Certification Systems (SCS), tests and certifies flooring products for compliance with indoor air quality emission requirements adopted in California. Flooring products include vinyl, linoleum, laminate flooring, wood flooring, ceramic flooring, rubber flooring, wall base, and associated sundries."	http://www. rfci.com/int_ FloorScore.htm
State of California Standard 1350, Section 9, Standard Practice for the Testing of Volatile Organic Emissions from Various Sources Using Small-Scale Environmental Chambers, Testing Criteria	This standard practice document specifies testing criteria for carpet emissions that will satisfy the credit requirements. According to the criteria, carpet must not exceed the maximum target emission factors used in the CRI Green Label program and follow the test protocol used by Green Label Plus. Test results submitted must be no more than 2 years old at the time of submission.	http://www. dhs.ca.gov/ps/ deodc/ehlb/iaq/ VOCS/ Section01350_ 7_15_2004_ FINAL_PLUS_ ADDENDUM -2004-01.pdfw

REFERENCE TITLE	REFERENCE DESCRIPTION	WEBSITE
California Department of Health Services Standard Practice for the Testing of Volatile Organic Emissions from Various Sources Using Small-Scale Environmental Chambers, including 2004 Addenda	This standard practice applies to any newly manufactured material generally used within an enclosed indoor environment. However, the testing practice excludes all products that cannot be tested whole or by representative sample in small-scale environmental chambers. The testing practice establishes the procedures for product sample collection, emissions testing, indoor concentration modeling, and documentation requirements associated with analyzing the emissions of volatile organic chemicals from various sources using small-scale environmental chambers. In addition, the testing practice lists target chemicals and their maximum allowable concentrations.	http://www.cal-iaq.org/VOC/Section01350_7_15_2004_FINAL_PLUS_ADDENDUM-2004-01.pdf
American National Standards Institute (ANSI)/Business and Institutional Furniture Makers' Association (BIFMA) X7.1–2007 Standard for Formaldehyde and TVOC Emissions of Low-Emitting Office Furniture Systems and Seating	ANSI/BIFMA X7.1–2007 "defines the criteria for office furniture VOC emissions to be classified as low-emitting product." Use it in conjunction with ANSI/BIFMA M7.1–2007.	http://www.bifma.org/standards/standards.html
Environmental Technology Verification (ETV) Large Chamber Test Protocol for Measuring Emissions of VOCs and Aldehydes, effective September 1999	Under the leadership of the EPA, a testing protocol committee developed the referenced standards. The protocol requires the placement of the seating product or furniture assembly to be tested in a climatically controlled chamber. A controlled quantity of conditioned air is drawn through the chamber, and emission concentrations are measured at set intervals over a four-day period.	http://www.epa.gov/etv/pdfs/vp/07_vp_furniture.pdf
GREENGUARD™ Certification Program	GEI has "established performance-based standards to define goods with low chemical and particle emissions for use indoors," primarily for building materials; interior furnishings; furniture; electronics; and cleaning, maintenance, and personal care products. The standard establishes certification procedures that include "test methods, allowable emissions levels, product sample collection and handling, testing type and frequency, and program application processes and acceptance."	http://www.greenguard.org
American National Standards Institute ANSI/ASHRAE Standard 55–2004: Thermal Environmental Conditions for Human Occupancy	ASHRAE 55–2004 identifies the factors of thermal comfort and the process for developing comfort criteria for a building space and its occupants. ASHRAE states, "This standard specifies the combinations of indoor space environment and personal factors that will produce thermal environmental conditions acceptable to 80% or more of the occupants within a space. The environmental factors addressed are temperature, thermal radiation, humidity and air speed; the personal factors are those of activity and clothing."	www.ashrae.org
Chartered Institute of Building Services Engineers (CIBSE) Applications Manual 10–2005, Natural Ventilation in Non-Domestic Buildings	CIBSE Applications Manual 10–2005 provides guidance for implementing natural ventilation in nonresidential buildings. It provides detailed information on how to adopt natural ventilation as the sole servicing strategy for a building or as an element in a mixed-mode design. According to the publisher, this manual "is a major revision of the Applications Manual (AM) first published in 1997. At the time, there was a significant expansion of interest in the application of engineered natural ventilation to the design of non-domestic buildings. The original AM10 sought to capture the state of knowledge as it existed in the mid-90s and present it in a form suited to the needs of every member of the	http://www.cibse.org

REFERENCE TITLE	REFERENCE DESCRIPTION	WEBSITE
	design team. Some 10 years on from the time when the initial manual was conceived, the state of knowledge has increased, and experience in the design and operation of naturally ventilated buildings has grown. This revision of AM10 is therefore a timely opportunity to update and enhance the guidance offered to designers and users of naturally ventilated buildings."	
ASHRAE HVAC Applications Handbook, 2003 Edition, Chapter 4 (Places of Assembly), Typical Natatorium Design Conditions	ASHRAE advances the science of heating, ventilation, air conditioning, and refrigeration for the public's benefit through research, standards writing, continuing education, and publications. The 2003 edition of the ASHRAE HVAC Applications Handbook contains "chapters on a broad range of applications, written to help design engineers use equipment and systems described in other handbook volumes."	http://www. ashrae.org
ASTM D1003 - 07e1, Standard Test Method for Haze and Luminous Transmittance of Transparent Plastics	This test method covers the evaluation of specific light-transmitting and wide-angle-light-scattering properties of planar sections of materials such as essentially transparent plastic.	http://www.astm. org
American National Standards Institute (ANSI)/ASA Standard S12.60-2002, Acoustical Performance Criteria, Design Requirements, and Guidelines for Schools	This standard provides acoustical performance criteria and design requirements for classrooms and other learning spaces. Annexes provide information on good design and construction practices, installation methods, and optional procedures to demonstrate conformance to the acoustical performance and design requirements of this standard. This standard seeks to provide design flexibility without compromising the goal of obtaining adequate speech intelligibility for all students and teachers in classrooms and learning spaces within the scope of the standard.	http://asastore. aip.org
ASHRAE Handbook, Chapter 47, Sound and Vibration Control, 2003 HVAC Applications	Because mechanical equipment is one of the major sources of noise in a building, the sound generated by mechanical equipment and its effects on the overall acoustical environment in a building must be considered. Mechanical equipment should be selected and equipment spaces designed with an emphasis on both the intended uses of the equipment and the goal of providing acceptable sound and vibration levels in occupied spaces of the building.	http://www. ashrae.org
Building Air Quality: A Guide for Building Owners and Facility Managers, EPA Reference Number 402–F–91–102, effective December 1991	Developed by the EPA and the National Institute for Occupational Safety and Health, this EPA publication details IAQ sources in buildings and methods to prevent and resolve IAQ problems.

According to the EPA, this guide provides information on factors affecting IAQ and describes how to develop and manage an IAQ profile. It offers strategies for identifying causes of IAQ problems, assessing alternative mitigation strategies, determining if a problem has been resolved, and deciding whether to consult outside technical specialists. Other topics included in the guide are "key problem causing factors; air quality sampling; heating, ventilation, and air conditioning (HVAC) systems; moisture problems; and additional sources of information." | http://www. epa.gov/iaq/ largebldgs/ baqtoc.html |

LEED 2009 for New Construction and Major Renovation

Project Checklist

Sustainable Sites — Possible Points: 26

Y	Prereq 1	Construction Activity Pollution Prevention	
	Credit 1	Site Selection	1
	Credit 2	Development Density and Community Connectivity	5
	Credit 3	Brownfield Redevelopment	1
	Credit 4.1	Alternative Transportation—Public Transportation Access	6
	Credit 4.2	Alternative Transportation—Bicycle Storage and Changing Rooms	1
	Credit 4.3	Alternative Transportation—Low-Emitting and Fuel-Efficient Vehicles	3
	Credit 4.4	Alternative Transportation—Parking Capacity	2
	Credit 5.1	Site Development—Protect or Restore Habitat	1
	Credit 5.2	Site Development—Maximize Open Space	1
	Credit 6.1	Stormwater Design—Quantity Control	1
	Credit 6.2	Stormwater Design—Quality Control	1
	Credit 7.1	Heat Island Effect—Non-roof	1
	Credit 7.2	Heat Island Effect—Roof	1
	Credit 8	Light Pollution Reduction	1

Water Efficiency — Possible Points: 10

Y	Prereq 1	Water Use Reduction—20% Reduction	
	Credit 1	Water Efficient Landscaping	2 to 4
	Credit 2	Innovative Wastewater Technologies	2
	Credit 3	Water Use Reduction	2 to 4

Energy and Atmosphere — Possible Points: 35

Y	Prereq 1	Fundamental Commissioning of Building Energy Systems	
Y	Prereq 2	Minimum Energy Performance	
Y	Prereq 3	Fundamental Refrigerant Management	
	Credit 1	Optimize Energy Performance	1 to 19
	Credit 2	On-Site Renewable Energy	1 to 7
	Credit 3	Enhanced Commissioning	2
	Credit 4	Enhanced Refrigerant Management	2
	Credit 5	Measurement and Verification	3
	Credit 6	Green Power	2

Materials and Resources — Possible Points: 14

Y	Prereq 1	Storage and Collection of Recyclables	
	Credit 1.1	Building Reuse—Maintain Existing Walls, Floors, and Roof	1 to 3
	Credit 1.2	Building Reuse—Maintain 50% of Interior Non-Structural Elements	1
	Credit 2	Construction Waste Management	1 to 2
	Credit 3	Materials Reuse	1 to 2

Materials and Resources, Continued

Y	N	?			
			Credit 4	Recycled Content	1 to 2
			Credit 5	Regional Materials	1 to 2
			Credit 6	Rapidly Renewable Materials	1
			Credit 7	Certified Wood	1

Indoor Environmental Quality — Possible Points: 15

Y	N	?			
Y			Prereq 1	Minimum Indoor Air Quality Performance	
Y			Prereq 2	Environmental Tobacco Smoke (ETS) Control	
			Credit 1	Outdoor Air Delivery Monitoring	1
			Credit 2	Increased Ventilation	1
			Credit 3.1	Construction IAQ Management Plan—During Construction	1
			Credit 3.2	Construction IAQ Management Plan—Before Occupancy	1
			Credit 4.1	Low-Emitting Materials—Adhesives and Sealants	1
			Credit 4.2	Low-Emitting Materials—Paints and Coatings	1
			Credit 4.3	Low-Emitting Materials—Flooring Systems	1
			Credit 4.4	Low-Emitting Materials—Composite Wood and Agrifiber Products	1
			Credit 5	Indoor Chemical and Pollutant Source Control	1
			Credit 6.1	Controllability of Systems—Lighting	1
			Credit 6.2	Controllability of Systems—Thermal Comfort	1
			Credit 7.1	Thermal Comfort—Design	1
			Credit 7.2	Thermal Comfort—Verification	1
			Credit 8.1	Daylight and Views—Daylight	1
			Credit 8.2	Daylight and Views—Views	1

Innovation and Design Process — Possible Points: 6

	Credit 1.1	Innovation in Design: Specific Title	1
	Credit 1.2	Innovation in Design: Specific Title	1
	Credit 1.3	Innovation in Design: Specific Title	1
	Credit 1.4	Innovation in Design: Specific Title	1
	Credit 1.5	Innovation in Design: Specific Title	1
	Credit 2	LEED Accredited Professional	1

Regional Priority Credits — Possible Points: 4

	Credit 1.1	Regional Priority: Specific Credit	1
	Credit 1.2	Regional Priority: Specific Credit	1
	Credit 1.3	Regional Priority: Specific Credit	1
	Credit 1.4	Regional Priority: Specific Credit	1

Total — Possible Points: 110

Certified 40 to 49 points   Silver 50 to 59 points   Gold 60 to 79 points   Platinum 80 to 110

LEED 2009 for Schools New Construction and Major Renovation

Project Checklist

Project Name

Date

Sustainable Sites — Possible Points: 24

		Y	N	?		
Prereq 1		Y			Construction Activity Pollution Prevention	
Prereq 1					Environmental Site Assessment	
Credit 1					Site Selection	1
Credit 2					Development Density and Community Connectivity	4
Credit 3					Brownfield Redevelopment	1
Credit 4.1					Alternative Transportation–Public Transportation Access	4
Credit 4.2					Alternative Transportation–Bicycle Storage and Changing Rooms	1
Credit 4.3					Alternative Transportation–Low-Emitting and Fuel-Efficient Vehicles	2
Credit 4.4					Alternative Transportation–Parking Capacity	2
Credit 5.1					Site Development–Protect or Restore Habitat	1
Credit 5.2					Site Development–Maximize Open Space	1
Credit 6.1					Stormwater Design–Quantity Control	1
Credit 6.2					Stormwater Design–Quality Control	1
Credit 7.1					Heat Island Effect–Non-roof	1
Credit 7.2					Heat Island Effect–Roof	1
Credit 8					Light Pollution Reduction	1
Credit 9					Site Master Plan	1
Credit 10					Joint Use of Facilities	1

Water Efficiency — Possible Points: 11

		Y	N	?		
Prereq 1		Y			Water Use Reduction—20% Reduction	
Credit 1					Water Efficient Landscaping	2 to 4
Credit 2					Innovative Wastewater Technologies	2
Credit 3					Water Use Reduction	2 to 4
Credit 3					Process Water Use Reduction	1

Energy and Atmosphere — Possible Points: 33

		Y	N	?		
Prereq 1		Y			Fundamental Commissioning of Building Energy Systems	
Prereq 2		Y			Minimum Energy Performance	
Prereq 3		Y			Fundamental Refrigerant Management	
Credit 1					Optimize Energy Performance	1 to 19
Credit 2					On-Site Renewable Energy	1 to 7
Credit 3					Enhanced Commissioning	2
Credit 4					Enhanced Refrigerant Management	1
Credit 5					Measurement and Verification	2
Credit 6					Green Power	2

Materials and Resources — Possible Points: 13

		Y	N	?		
Prereq 1		Y			Storage and Collection of Recyclables	
Credit 1.1					Building Reuse—Maintain Existing Walls, Floors, and Roof	1 to 2
Credit 1.2					Building Reuse—Maintain 50% of Interior Non-Structural Elements	1
Credit 2					Construction Waste Management	1 to 2

Materials and Resources, Continued

		Y	N	?		
Credit 3					Materials Reuse	1 to 2
Credit 4					Recycled Content	1 to 2
Credit 5					Regional Materials	1 to 2
Credit 6					Rapidly Renewable Materials	1
Credit 7					Certified Wood	1

Indoor Environmental Quality — Possible Points: 19

		Y	N	?		
Prereq 1		Y			Minimum Indoor Air Quality Performance	
Prereq 2		Y			Environmental Tobacco Smoke (ETS) Control	
Prereq 3		Y			Minimum Acoustical Performance	
Credit 1					Outdoor Air Delivery Monitoring	1
Credit 2					Increased Ventilation	1
Credit 3.1					Construction IAQ Management Plan–During Construction	1
Credit 3.2					Construction IAQ Management Plan–Before Occupancy	1
Credit 4					Low-Emitting Materials	1 to 4
Credit 5					Indoor Chemical and Pollutant Source Control	1
Credit 6.1					Controllability of Systems—Lighting	1
Credit 6.2					Controllability of Systems—Thermal Comfort	1
Credit 7.1					Thermal Comfort—Design	1
Credit 7.2					Thermal Comfort—Verification	1
Credit 8.1					Daylight and Views–Daylight	1 to 3
Credit 8.2					Daylight and Views–Views	1
Credit 9					Enhanced Acoustical Performance	1
Credit 10					Mold Prevention	1

Innovation and Design Process — Possible Points: 6

Credit 1.1		Innovation in Design: Specific Title	1
Credit 1.2		Innovation in Design: Specific Title	1
Credit 1.3		Innovation in Design: Specific Title	1
Credit 1.4		Innovation in Design: Specific Title	1
Credit 2		LEED Accredited Professional	1
Credit 3		The School as a Teaching Tool	1

Regional Priority Credits — Possible Points: 4

Credit 1.1		Regional Priority: Specific Credit	1
Credit 1.2		Regional Priority: Specific Credit	1
Credit 1.3		Regional Priority: Specific Credit	1
Credit 1.4		Regional Priority: Specific Credit	1

Total — Possible Points: 110

Certified 40 to 49 points   Silver 50 to 59 points   Gold 60 to 79 points   Platinum 80 to 110 points

LEED 2009 for Core and Shell Development

Project Checklist

Project Name

Date

Sustainable Sites — Possible Points: 28

Y	N	?			
Y			Prereq 1	Construction Activity Pollution Prevention	
			Credit 1	Site Selection	1
			Credit 2	Development Density and Community Connectivity	5
			Credit 3	Brownfield Redevelopment	1
			Credit 4.1	Alternative Transportation—Public Transportation Access	6
			Credit 4.2	Alternative Transportation—Bicycle Storage and Changing Rooms	2
			Credit 4.3	Alternative Transportation—Low-Emitting and Fuel-Efficient Vehicles	3
			Credit 4.4	Alternative Transportation—Parking Capacity	2
			Credit 5.1	Site Development—Protect or Restore Habitat	1
			Credit 5.2	Site Development—Maximize Open Space	1
			Credit 6.1	Stormwater Design—Quantity Control	1
			Credit 6.2	Stormwater Design—Quality Control	1
			Credit 7.1	Heat Island Effect—Non-roof	1
			Credit 7.2	Heat Island Effect—Roof	1
			Credit 8	Light Pollution Reduction	1
			Credit 9	Tenant Design and Construction Guidelines	1

Water Efficiency — Possible Points: 10

Y	N	?			
Y			Prereq 1	Water Use Reduction—20% Reduction	
			Credit 1	Water Efficient Landscaping	2 to 4
			Credit 2	Innovative Wastewater Technologies	2
			Credit 3	Water Use Reduction	2 to 4

Energy and Atmosphere — Possible Points: 37

Y	N	?			
Y			Prereq 1	Fundamental Commissioning of Building Energy Systems	
Y			Prereq 2	Minimum Energy Performance	
Y			Prereq 3	Fundamental Refrigerant Management	
			Credit 1	Optimize Energy Performance	3 to 21
			Credit 2	On-Site Renewable Energy	4
			Credit 3	Enhanced Commissioning	2
			Credit 4	Enhanced Refrigerant Management	2
			Credit 5.1	Measurement and Verification—Base Building	3
			Credit 5.2	Measurement and Verification—Tenant Submetering	3
			Credit 6	Green Power	2

Materials and Resources — Possible Points: 13

Y	N	?			
Y			Prereq 1	Storage and Collection of Recyclables	
			Credit 1	Building Reuse—Maintain Existing Walls, Floors, and Roof	1 to 5
			Credit 2	Construction Waste Management	1 to 2
			Credit 3	Materials Reuse	1
			Credit 4	Recycled Content	1 to 2
			Credit 5	Regional Materials	1 to 2
			Credit 6	Certified Wood	1

Indoor Environmental Quality — Possible Points: 12

Y	N	?			
Y			Prereq 1	Minimum Indoor Air Quality Performance	
Y			Prereq 2	Environmental Tobacco Smoke (ETS) Control	
			Credit 1	Outdoor Air Delivery Monitoring	1
			Credit 2	Increased Ventilation	1
			Credit 3	Construction IAQ Management Plan—During Construction	1
			Credit 4.1	Low-Emitting Materials—Adhesives and Sealants	1
			Credit 4.2	Low-Emitting Materials—Paints and Coatings	1
			Credit 4.3	Low-Emitting Materials—Flooring Systems	1
			Credit 4.4	Low-Emitting Materials—Composite Wood and Agrifiber Products	1
			Credit 5	Indoor Chemical and Pollutant Source Control	1
			Credit 6	Controllability of Systems—Thermal Comfort	1
			Credit 7	Thermal Comfort—Design	1
			Credit 8.1	Daylight and Views—Daylight	1
			Credit 8.2	Daylight and Views—Views	1

Innovation and Design Process — Possible Points: 6

Y	N	?			
			Credit 1.1	Innovation in Design: Specific Title	1
			Credit 1.2	Innovation in Design: Specific Title	1
			Credit 1.3	Innovation in Design: Specific Title	1
			Credit 1.4	Innovation in Design: Specific Title	1
			Credit 1.5	Innovation in Design: Specific Title	1
			Credit 2	LEED Accredited Professional	1

Regional Priority Credits — Possible Points: 4

Y	N	?			
			Credit 1.1	Regional Priority: Specific Credit	1
			Credit 1.2	Regional Priority: Specific Credit	1
			Credit 1.3	Regional Priority: Specific Credit	1
			Credit 1.4	Regional Priority: Specific Credit	1

Total — Possible Points: 110

Certified 40 to 49 points   Silver 50 to 59 points   Gold 60 to 79 points   Platinum 80 to 110